Dear Adult Student,

Learning new things and building basic skills may be challenging for you, but they also can be very exciting. When you follow the guidelines for learning basic skills, you will be acquiring skills that will prepare you for life.

The skills that you will study and practice in this workbook will help you become more confident as you master them. These skills can help you with many things that you do in life, such as buying a car, shopping for groceries, applying for a job, reading maps, and recognizing signs.

You may be using this workbook on your own or as part of an adult education or training program that you are enrolled in. If this is your own copy, you may want to answer the practice questions right in the workbook or on the attached answer sheet in the back. If the workbook belongs to the classroom or program that you are enrolled in and will be used by other students, you should not write in it. Use a separate answer sheet instead.

Before you start your work, it would be helpful to find out which skills you need to work on. You may have taken a test such as TABE®—*Tests of Adult Basic Education*. These tests can be used to find out what skills you already know, and also to point out which skills need more work.

Once you have identified the skills you need to work on, go to the Table of Contents, find the section for one of the skills that you want to work on, turn to that page, and start doing the practice questions.

When you have finished the practice questions, you will find an answer key at the back of the workbook. You can use the answer key to check your work.

Best wishes for a successful and useful experience in using this workbook to get information and practice on the skills that you want to learn more about and would like to master. Congratulations on continuing your education.

Mastering the skills listed below can help you achieve your goals and improve many life skills, from reading the daily newspaper to getting a better job. Talk with your teacher about the skills that you need to work on. Find a skill section that you want to work on in the list below, turn to that section in your workbook, and start practicing.

The answers to the problems in each section are located in the Answer Key in the back of this workbook.

DECIMALS

A *decimal* is a number that represents part of a whole. Decimals are another way of writing fractions that have denominators that are powers of ten. For example, 0.257 is the same as $\frac{257}{1,000}$.

Decimals includes subskills, such as Addition, Subtraction, Multiplication, and Division.

Look at these examples of decimals. Choose your answer for each problem.

EXAMPLE	ANSWER
0.7 − 0.22 =	• **Answer a** is **not** correct. This is the result of the subtraction problem 0.07 − 0.22.
a ⁻0.15	
b 0.48	• **Answer b** is correct. The first decimal can be written as 0.70. Then the problem can be written in vertical format before subtracting:
c 0.52	
d 0.58	
e None of these	

$$
\begin{array}{r}
0.70 \\
-\ 0.22 \\
\hline
0.48
\end{array}
$$

- **Answer c** is **not** correct. The digits in the hundredths place were added instead of subtracted.

- **Answer d** is **not** correct. No regrouping was done.

EXAMPLE	ANSWER

$23.04 \div 36 =$

a   1.5625

b   15.625

c   0.64

d   6.4

e   None of these

- **Answer *a*** is **not** correct. This is the result of $36 \div 23.04$.

- **Answer *b*** is **not** correct. This is the result of $36 \div 2.304$.

- **Answer *c*** is correct

$$
\begin{array}{r}
0.64 \\
36\overline{)23.04} \\
216 \\
\hline
144 \\
144 \\
\hline
0
\end{array}
$$

- **Answer *d*** is **not** correct. The decimal point is incorrectly placed.

When adding or subtracting decimals, line up the decimal points. For example, write

 instead of

$$
\begin{array}{r}
32.8 \\
-\ 2.035
\end{array}
\qquad
\begin{array}{r}
32.8 \\
-\ 2.035
\end{array}
$$

Reminder

Do these decimal problems.
First, try Numbers 1 and 2 for practice.

1. $0.06 + 0.775 =$

   a   0.781

   b   1.375

   c   0.845

   d   0.835

   e   None of these

ANSWER *d* is correct. $0.06 + 0.775 = 0.835$

2.   16.1
     $\times$ 4.7

   a   65.67

   b   51.67

   c   75.67

   d   71.67

   e   None of these

ANSWER *c* is correct. $16.1 \times 4.7 = 75.67$

Now you are ready to do more problems. The answers to the problems in this section can be found in the back of this workbook.

3.   43.84
     + 29.672

    a 73.512

    b 73.412

    c 73.238

    d 73.438

    e None of these

4. 534.32 + 42.2 =

    a   57.652

    b 492.12

    c 538.54

    d 956.32

    e None of these

Reminder

When adding, subtracting, or multiplying decimals, it is often helpful to rewrite the problem in vertical format. For example, the problem 31.4 + 25.6 can be written as follows:

$$\begin{array}{r} 31.4 \\ + 25.6 \\ \hline \end{array}$$

5.   7.5
    − 0.49

   a 7.19

   b 7.01

   c 6.11

   d 2.6

   e None of these

6.   0.209
    − 0.183

   a 0.126

   b 0.026

   c 0.116

   d 0.016

   e None of these

Apply

Decimals are useful whenever precise measurements are needed. For instance, engine parts typically need to be manufactured to an accuracy of a few thousandths of an inch. You might also need to use decimals at the grocery store. If the price of wild Alaskan salmon is $7.49 per pound and you buy 1.35 pounds, how much will the salmon cost?

7.   0.8
       × 0.7

     a   0.56

     b   56.0

     c   5.6

     d   0.056

     e   None of these

8. $0.527 \times 100 =$

     a   527.0

     b   52.7

     c   5.27

     d   0.527

     e   None of these

Apply

When multiplying decimals, add the number of decimal places in each factor. That total tells you how many decimal places will be in the answer. For example:

1.003	3 places
× 0.15	+ 2 places
5015	
1003	
0.15045	5 places

9. 0.14)‾82.46‾

    a   58.9

    b 589.0

    c   50.89

    d   5.89

    e None of these

10. 0.01)‾45‾

    a   0.45

    b   4.5

    c   45

    d 450

    e None of these

When dividing by a decimal, make the divisor a whole number by multiplying it by a power of ten. Multiply the dividend by the same power of ten, then divide. For example: $\frac{37.1}{2.4}$ may be multiplied by $\frac{10}{10}$, changing it to $\frac{371}{24}$ before dividing.

For Numbers 11 through 14, write your answers.

11. $32.706 + 0.4102 + 9.08 =$ _____

12. $12.027 - 6.04 =$ _____

13. $1.04 \times 1.05 =$ _____

14. $0.27 \div 1.2 =$ _____

FRACTIONS

A *fraction* is a number that represents a part of a whole that has been divided into equal parts. If a pie is divided into 8 equal pieces and you eat 2 of them, you have eaten $\frac{2}{8}$ (or $\frac{1}{4}$) of the pie.

You can also think of a fraction as a ratio between two whole numbers, or a division problem. For instance, the fraction $\frac{20}{4}$ is another way to write $20 \div 4$.

Fractions include subskills, such as Addition, Subtraction, Multiplication, and Division.

Look at these examples of fractions. Choose your answer for each problem.

EXAMPLE	ANSWER

EXAMPLE

$\frac{2}{5} + \frac{9}{10} =$

a $\frac{11}{15}$

b $1\frac{1}{10}$

c $\frac{13}{20}$

d $1\frac{2}{5}$

e None of these

ANSWER

- **Answer *a* is not** correct. The fractions were not rewritten with a common denominator, and the numerators and denominators were simply added.

- **Answer *b* is not** correct. The fraction $\frac{2}{5}$ was rewritten as $\frac{2}{10}$ instead of $\frac{4}{10}$.

- **Answer *c* is not** correct. The fraction $\frac{2}{5}$ was correctly rewritten as $\frac{4}{10}$, but the denominators were added as well as the numerators.

- **Answer *d* is not** correct. The fraction $\frac{2}{5}$ was correctly rewritten as $\frac{4}{10}$, but $\frac{4}{10}$ and $\frac{9}{10}$ were added incorrectly.

- **Answer *e* is correct.** The correct answer, $\frac{13}{10}$, is not given. The fraction $\frac{2}{5}$ can be rewritten as $\frac{4}{10}$. Then the fractions can be added: $\frac{4}{10} + \frac{9}{10} = \frac{13}{10}$, or $1\frac{3}{10}$.

EXAMPLE	ANSWER

$8 \div \frac{4}{7} =$

a $\frac{32}{7}$

b $\frac{1}{14}$

c $\frac{7}{32}$

d   14

e   None of these

- **Answer *a*** is **not** correct. The numbers were multiplied instead of divided.

- **Answer *b*** is **not** correct. The 8 was written as a fraction ($\frac{8}{1}$) and then inverted instead of the second fraction.

- **Answer *c*** is **not** correct. Both numbers were inverted before multiplying.

- **Answer *d*** is correct. To divide with fractions, invert the second fraction (the divisor) and multiply as follows:

$$8 \div \frac{4}{7} = \frac{8}{1} \times \frac{7}{4} = \frac{56}{4} = 14$$

Fractions are often used in recipes ($\frac{1}{4}$ cup of sugar), measurements ($3\frac{1}{4}$ inches of ribbon, $\frac{3}{4}$ pound of hamburger), and observations (the stadium is $\frac{1}{2}$ full).

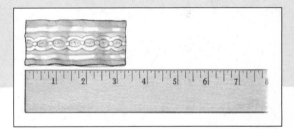

Do these fraction problems.
First, try Numbers 1 and 2 for practice.

1. $\frac{8}{3} + \frac{11}{6} =$

    a $\frac{9}{2}$

    b   9

    c $\frac{19}{9}$

    d $\frac{19}{6}$

    e   None of these

ANSWER *a* is correct. The fractions should be written with a common denominator, then added. $\frac{8}{3} + \frac{11}{6} = \frac{16}{6} + \frac{11}{6} = \frac{27}{6} = \frac{9}{2}$

2. $\frac{1}{6} \div \frac{2}{3} =$

    a $\frac{1}{9}$

    b $\frac{1}{4}$

    c   9

    d   4

    e   None of these

ANSWER *b* is correct. $\frac{1}{6} \div \frac{2}{3} = \frac{1}{6} \times \frac{3}{2} = \frac{3}{12} = \frac{1}{4}$

Now you are ready to do more problems. The answers to the problems in this section can be found in the back of this workbook.

3. $\frac{2}{4} + \frac{4}{4} =$

   a $\frac{1}{2}$

   b $\frac{3}{4}$

   c $1\frac{1}{3}$

   d 2

   e None of these

4. $1\frac{2}{3} + 3\frac{3}{4} =$

   a $4\frac{7}{12}$

   b 5

   c $4\frac{5}{7}$

   d $5\frac{5}{12}$

   e None of these

The value of a fraction is unchanged if the numerator and denominator are multiplied or divided by the number 1 written in a different form, such as $\frac{2}{2}$ or $\frac{7}{7}$.

Reminder

5. $\frac{9}{16} - \frac{3}{16} =$

    a $\frac{1}{3}$

    b $\frac{3}{4}$

    c $\frac{3}{8}$

    d $\frac{3}{16}$

    e None of these

6. $\frac{3}{4} - \frac{1}{5} =$

    a $\frac{1}{2}$

    b $\frac{1}{10}$

    c $\frac{9}{20}$

    d $\frac{11}{20}$

    e None of these

Reminder

To add or subtract fractions with different denominators, begin by finding a common denominator. Then add or subtract. For example:

$$\frac{1}{3} + \frac{1}{5} = \frac{5}{15} + \frac{3}{15} = \frac{8}{15}$$

7. $\frac{2}{3} \times \frac{3}{10} =$

    a $\frac{1}{10}$

    b $\frac{6}{5}$

    c $\frac{1}{30}$

    d $\frac{2}{5}$

    e None of these

8. $\frac{5}{4} \times \frac{10}{3} =$

    a $\frac{25}{3}$

    b $\frac{25}{6}$

    c $\frac{2}{5}$

    d $\frac{5}{12}$

    e None of these

When reducing fractions before multiplying, remember to divide a numerator and a denominator by the same number. In this example, a 3 is divided into a numerator and into a denominator.

$$\frac{{}^{1}\cancel{3}}{2} \times \frac{7}{\cancel{15}_{5}} = \frac{7}{10}$$

Reminder

9. $\frac{4}{5} \div \frac{1}{5} =$

   a $\frac{4}{25}$

   b $\frac{1}{4}$

   c $6\frac{1}{4}$

   d   4

   e   None of these

10. $2\frac{1}{2} \times \frac{4}{5} =$

   a   2

   b $2\frac{2}{5}$

   c $2\frac{5}{8}$

   d $2\frac{1}{2}$

   e   None of these

For Numbers 11 through 14, write your answers.

11. $1\frac{7}{8} + 2\frac{3}{5} =$ _____

12. $4\frac{5}{8} - 2\frac{5}{16} =$ _____

13. $\frac{11}{24} \times 6 =$ _____

14. $\frac{14}{9} \div \frac{7}{12} =$ _____

INTEGERS

Integers are all the whole numbers and their opposites. Numbers such as
16, $^-40$, and 0 are integers. Fractions such as $\frac{1}{2}$ and decimals such as $^-4.5$
are not integers.

Integers includes subskills, such as Addition,
Subtraction, Multiplication, and Division.

Look at these examples of integers.
Choose your answer for each problem.

EXAMPLE	ANSWER
$^-6 + (^-12) =$	• **Answer *a*** is **not** correct. When two negative numbers are added, the result is negative.
a 18	
b 6	• **Answer *b*** is **not** correct. This would be the answer to $^-6 + 12$.
c $^-6$	
d $^-18$	• **Answer *c*** is **not** correct. This would be the answer to $6 + (^-12)$.
e None of these	
	• **Answer *d*** is correct. Since $^-6$ and $^-12$ are negative, and $6 + 12 = 18$, the answer is $^-18$.

EXAMPLE	ANSWER
$50 \div (^-25) =$ *a* $^-2$ *b* $^-25$ *c* 2 *d* 25 *e* None of these	• **Answer *a* is correct.** A positive number divided by a negative number results in a negative answer. Since $50 \div 25 = 2$, the answer is $^-2$. • **Answer *b* is not correct.** The numbers were added and signed incorrectly. • **Answer *c* is not correct.** The answer should be negative, not positive. • **Answer *d* is not correct.** The numbers were added instead of divided.

The absolute value of a number is its distance from zero without regard to its direction. For example, the absolute value of $^-15$, which is written as $|^-15|$, is 15. Notice that $|15|$ is also 15.

Reminder

Do these integer problems.
First, try Numbers 1 and 2 for practice.

1. $^-7 - 9 =$

   a   2

   b $^-2$

   c   16

   d $^-16$

   e   None of these

ANSWER *d* is correct. To subtract integers, add the opposite of the subtrahend and follow the addition rules. $^-7 - 9 = {}^-7 + {}^-9 = {}^-16$

2. $^-12 \times {}^-7 =$

   a $^-72$

   b $^-84$

   c   72

   d   84

   e   None of these

ANSWER *d* is correct. When two negative numbers are multiplied, the answer is positive. We know that $12 \times 7 = 84$. So that means $^-12 \times {}^-7 = 84$.

Now you are ready to do more problems. The answers to the problems in this section can be found in the back of this workbook.

3. $-3 + 2 =$

   a   5

   b   1

   c -5

   d -1

   e   None of these

Apply

Negative integers are used when temperatures drop below zero. When the temperature is $-10°F$, it's very cold. Negative integers can also be used to describe sea depths. A depth of -75 feet means "75 feet below sea level."

4. $14 + (^-7) =$

    a $^-7$

    b $^-21$

    c   7

    d   21

    e None of these

5. $16 - (^-13) =$

    a   3

    b $^-3$

    c   29

    d $^-29$

    e None of these

Apply

When adding with unlike signs, subtract the absolute values and keep the original sign of the number with the larger absolute value. For example, to add $^-15 + 9$:

$$|^-15| - |9| = 15 - 9 = 6$$

The original sign of the number with the larger absolute value ($^-15$) is negative. Therefore, the answer is negative.

$$^-15 + 9 = {}^-6$$

6. $8 \times {}^-11 =$

    a ${}^-88$

    b   88

    c   19

    d ${}^-3$

    e   None of these

7. ${}^-4 - ({}^-10) =$

    a   6

    b ${}^-6$

    c   14

    d ${}^-14$

    e   None of these

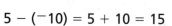

Subtracting a negative number is the same as adding a positive number. For example:

$$5 - ({}^-10) = 5 + 10 = 15$$

8. $^-16 \times {}^-16 =$

   a   0

   b $^-32$

   c   256

   d $^-256$

   e None of these

9. $^-24 \div {}^-3 =$

   a $^-6$

   b $^-8$

   c   6

   d   8

   e None of these

10. $^-40 \div 5 =$

   a $^-8$

   b $^-9$

   c   8

   d   9

   e None of these

Reminder

When multiplying or dividing with the same sign, the result is positive. When multiplying or dividing with different signs, the result is negative.

For Numbers 11 through 14, write your answers.

11. $^-40 + {}^-10 = $ _____

12. $| 200 - 600 | = $ _____

13. $^-4 \times {}^-5 \times {}^-6 = $ _____

14. $^-45 \div {}^-45 = $ _____

PERCENTS

The *percent* symbol (%) originated from the number "100."

The symbol means "per hundred," "divided by 100," or "multiplied by $\frac{1}{100}$."

For example, 16% means 16 per 100, $\frac{16}{100}$, or $16 \times \frac{1}{100}$.

Percents includes subskills, such as Percents.

Look at these examples of percents.
Choose your answer for each problem.

EXAMPLE	ANSWER
2% of 300 =	• **Answer *a*** is **not** correct. This is 0.2% of 300.
a 0.6	
b 1.5	• **Answer *b*** is **not** correct. The number 300 was divided by 200 instead of multiplied by 0.02.
c 6	
d 15	• **Answer *c*** is correct. To find 2% of 300, change 2% to a decimal, then multiply: 0.02 × 300 = 6.
e None of these	
	• **Answer *d*** is **not** correct. The number 300 was divided by 20 instead of multiplied by 0.02.

You can use percents to calculate a 25% discount, 6% sales tax, or a 15% tip. Percents greater than 100 are useful, too. If the population of a city grows from 10,000 to 40,000, the increase is 300%.

EXAMPLE	ANSWER

75% of = 9

a 6.75

b 12

c 67.5

d 120

e None of these

- **Answer *a* is not** correct. This is 75% of 9.

- **Answer *b* is correct.** To find the answer, divide 9 by 0.75.

- **Answer *c* is not** correct. Nine has been multiplied by 7.5 instead of divided by 0.75.

- **Answer *d* is not** correct. A decimal point has been misplaced.

To change a percent to its decimal form, drop the percent symbol and move the decimal point two places to the left. For example:

17% = 0.17
6% = 0.06
325% = 3.25
0.5% = 0.005

Do these percent problems.
First, try Numbers 1 and 2 for practice.

1. 80% of 35 =

   a   2.8

   b   0.28

   c 280.0

   d 28.0

   e None of these

   ANSWER **d** is correct. To find the answer, 80% can be converted to the decimal 0.8, then multiplied by 35.

$$0.8 \times 35 = 28.0$$

2. What percent of $27.00 is $1.35?

   a 5%

   b 2%

   c 0.5%

   d 0.2%

   e None of these

   ANSWER **a** is correct. First divide $1.35 by $27.00, then convert the result to a percent:

$$27\overline{)1.35}^{\,0.05}$$

   The answer is 5%, because 0.05 = 5%.

Now you are ready to do more problems. The answers to the problems in this section can be found in the back of this workbook.

3. 6% of $3.00 =

    a $0.50

    b $5.00

    c $1.80

    d $18.00

    e   None of these

To find a percentage of an amount, change the percent to a decimal or fraction, then multiply. For example:

$$12\% \text{ of } 40 = 0.12 \times 40 = 4.8$$

or

$$\frac{12}{100} \times 40 = \frac{3}{25} \times 40 = \frac{24}{5} = 4\frac{4}{5}$$

Reminder

4. 4.8% of 80 =

    a 384.0

    b 38.4

    c   0.384

    d   3.84

    e None of these

5. What percent of 75 is 60?

    a   0.8%

    b   1.25%

    c 12.5%

    d 80%

    e None of these

Apply

To solve the problem "What percent of 200 is 50?", first write the fraction $\frac{50}{200}$. Next, find the equivalent fraction that has a denominator of 100. Since $\frac{50}{200} = \frac{25}{100}$, the answer is 25%. Another way to solve this problem is to first divide 50 by 200. Then, convert the decimal answer to a percent.

$$\frac{50}{200} = 0.25 = 25\%$$

6. What percent of 36 is 45?

   a 80%

   b 90%

   c 125%

   d 133%

   e None of these

7. 90% of ☐ = 12.6

   a 11.34

   b 13.5

   c 14

   d 16

   e None of these

To solve a problem such as 35% of ☐ = 140, change 35% to its decimal form (0.35) and divide it into 140.

$$\frac{140}{0.35} = \frac{14{,}000}{35} = 400$$

8. 150% of ☐ = 900

    a   600

    b   1,350

    c   6,000

    d 13,500

    e None of these

9. $1\frac{1}{2}$% of ☐ = $6

    a $40

    b $90

    c $400

    d $900

    e None of these

For Numbers 10 through 13, write your answers.

10. 0.4% of 20 = _____

11. What percent of \$5.00 is \$0.25? _____

12. 8% of ☐ = \$1.76 _____

13. 0.5% of ☐ = 8 _____

ORDER OF OPERATIONS

The *order of operations* was established so that expressions containing more than one operation would be evaluated the same way by any person. The order of operations contains a set of rules that must be followed in the exact order given as shown below:

1) Simplify expressions contained within grouping symbols, such as parentheses and brackets.
2) Evaluate all exponents.
3) Do all multiplication and division from left to right. Perform the operation as soon as it appears.
4) Do all addition and subtraction from left to right. Perform the operation as soon as it appears.

Order of Operations includes subskills, such as Order of Operations.

Look at this example of order of operations. Choose your answer.

EXAMPLE	ANSWER
$6 - 4 \div 2 + 3 - 3 \times 2 =$ *a* ⁻2 *b* 4 *c* 5 *d* 1 *e* None of these	• **Answer *a* is not** correct. Division and multiplication must be done before subtraction and addition. In this case, $- 4 \div 2$ should be done before $6 - 4$. • **Answer *b* is not** correct. Division and multiplication must be done before subtraction and addition. In this case, $3 - 3$ was subtracted, and 3×2 should be multiplied first. • **Answer *c* is not** correct. When a negative number is divided or multiplied by a positive number, the result is a negative number. • **Answer *d* is correct.** First divide, $- 4 \div 2$. Then multiply -3×2 and add or subtract the resulting numbers from left to right: $6 - 2 + 3 - 6 = 1$.

Do these order of operations problems. First, try Numbers 1 and 2 for practice.

1. $^-(3)^2 + 8 \div 2 \times 4 =$

   a   10

   b   7

   c   25

   d $^-8$

   e   None of these

ANSWER *b* is correct. Since the negative sign is outside the parentheses, it does not get squared with the 3. Therefore, $^-(3)^2 = {}^-9$. Division or multiplication must be performed from left to right (whichever appears first), so $8 \div 2 \times 4 = 4 \times 4 = 16$. Then combine the results: $^-9 + 16 = 7$.

2. $3(9 + 3^2) \div 3 \times {}^-3 =$

   a $^-6$

   b $^-54$

   c $^-5$

   d $^-48$

   e   None of these

ANSWER *b* is **correct**. Using the order of operations, perform operations inside the parentheses by converting the exponents first: $3^2 = 9$, then $9 + 9 = 18$. Next, perform all multiplication or division from left to right, whichever appears first: $3 \times 18 = 54$; $54 \div 3 = 18$; $18 \times {}^-3 = {}^-54$.

Now you are ready to do more problems. The answers to the problems in this section can be found in the back of this workbook.

3. $(26 \div 2 - 3)^2 =$

    a $^-676$

    b   160

    c   676

    d   100

    e   None of these

4. $8 + 4(3) \div 6 - 2 =$

    a   4

    b   9

    c   8

    d   5

    e   None of these

5. $8^2 - 8^2 \div 4(2) =$

    a   32

    b   0

    c   56

    d   96

    e   None of these

6. $3 \times 8 - 4 \div 2 =$

   a   10

   b   22

   c   6

   d   18

   e   None of these

7. $40 \div 2^3 + 2 \times 4 - 1 =$

   a   12

   b   15

   c   11

   d   21

   e   None of these

8. $(18 \div 9 - 9) \times 3 - 2^2 =$

   a $^-25$

   b   7

   c $^-49$

   d $^-17$

   e   None of these

9. $32 \div 4 \times 2 + 4 \div 2 =$

   a   6

   b   10

   c   18

   d   24

   e   None of these

10. $14 - (^-7) + 14 \div 7 =$

   a   23

   b   5

   c $^-1$

   d   9

   e   None of these

For Numbers 11 through 14, write your answers.

11. $-108 \div (-2) \div 6 - 1 =$

   _____

12. $56 \div 7 - 4 \times {}^-2 =$

   _____

13. $2^2 \div 4 + 13 - 4 \times 2 =$

   _____

14. $36 \div 6 + 88 \div 11 \times 2 =$

   _____

ALGEBRAIC OPERATIONS

When we do *algebra*, we use letters (or variables) to represent numbers.

We use algebraic operations to work with expressions such as $3(7x - 2)$.

Algebraic Operations includes subskills, such as Computation with Exponents, Solve Equations, and Simplify Expressions.

Look at these examples of algebraic operations. Choose your answer for each problem.

EXAMPLE	ANSWER

$9^2 \times 9^3 =$

a 9^5

b 9^6

c 81^5

d 81^6

e   None of these

- **Answer a** is correct. When multiplying exponential expressions with the same base, add the exponents and keep the base: $9^2 \times 9^3 = 9^5$.

- **Answer b** is **not** correct. The exponents were multiplied instead of added.

- **Answer c** is **not** correct. The base of the result should be 9. In this case, the bases were multiplied.

- **Answer d** is **not** correct. The bases were multiplied and the exponents were multiplied instead of added.

Knowing how to use algebraic operations helps you work with formulas.

For example, to convert a temperature in degrees Celsius to degrees Fahrenheit, you can use the formula $F = \frac{9}{5}C + 32$.

EXAMPLE	ANSWER

$6x(2x - 1) =$

a $6x$

b $11x^2$

c $12x^2 - 1$

d $12x^2 - 6x$

e None of these

- **Answer a** is **not** correct. The terms $6x$ and $2x$ were multiplied incorrectly to get a result of $12x$ instead of $12x^2$. Then $12x - 6x = 6x$.

- **Answer b** is **not** correct. Only the $2x$ term was multiplied by $6x$, and the 1 was subtracted incorrectly.

- **Answer c** is **not** correct. Only the $2x$ term was multiplied by $6x$.

- **Answer d** is correct. The distributive property is used, multiplying $6x$ by $2x$, then $6x$ by -1 to get $12x^2 - 6x$. Since $12x^2$ and $6x$ are not like terms, the expression cannot be simplified further.

When exponents are used with a number, such as 4^5, 4 is called the *base* and 5 is called the *exponent*.

Reminder

Do these algebraic operations problems.
First, try Numbers 1 and 2 for practice.

1. $10^3 \times 10^3 =$

    a 10^6

    b 10^9

    c 100^6

    d 100^9

    e   None of these

ANSWER *a* is correct. The exponents are added and the base stays the same.

2. $(2x + 1)(2x + 3) =$

    a $4x^2 + 3$

    b $4x^2 + 2x + 3$

    c $4x^2 + 6x + 3$

    d $4x^2 + 8x + 3$

    e   None of these

ANSWER *d* is correct. We can use the FOIL (First, Outer, Inner, Last) method shown below.

$$(2x + 1)(2x + 3) = 4x^2 + 6x + 2x + 3 = 4x^2 + 8x + 3$$

Now you are ready to do more problems. The answers to the problems in this section can be found in the back of this workbook.

3. $8^{15} \div 8^3 =$

    a 8^5

    b   1

    c 8^{12}

    d   5

    e   None of these

When dividing exponential expressions with the same base, subtract the exponents (*dividend exponent − divisor exponent*) and keep the base. For example:

$$3^7 \div 3^2 = 3^{7-2} = 3^5$$

4. $(10^2)^6 =$

   a 10^3

   b 10^4

   c 10^8

   d 10^{64}

   e None of these

When an exponential expression is raised to another power, keep the base and multiply the exponents. For example:

$$(7^2)^5 = 7^{10}$$

5. $5x + 3x =$

   a $8x$

   b $15x^2$

   c $8 + x$

   d $8x^2$

   e   None of these

6. $8y - y =$

   a 7

   b 8

   c $7y$

   d $-8y^2$

   e   None of these

If two or more terms have the same variable and the same exponent, they are called *like terms*. Like terms can be added or subtracted.
For example:

$$18x^2 - x^2 = 17x^2 \quad \text{and} \quad 3ab + 7ab = 10ab$$

Unlike terms cannot be added or subtracted, so an expression such as $9x^3 - 6x$ cannot be combined.

7. $4(2b + 5) =$

    a $6b + 5$

    b $6b + 20$

    c $8b + 5$

    d $8b + 20$

    e None of these

8. $2x + 3x(4 - y) =$

    a $20x - 5y$

    b $14x - 3y$

    c $20x - 5xy$

    d $14x - 3xy$

    e None of these

Reminder

Use the distributive property with expressions involving parentheses. After you use the distributive property, combine like terms. For example:

$$6x - 2(x - 5) = 6x - 2x + 10 = 4x + 10$$

9. $\dfrac{6y^2 + 14y}{2y} =$

   a $10y$

   b $17y$

   c $13y^2$

   d $3y + 7$

   e None of these

10. $(3a - 5)^2 =$

   a $6a^2 - 8a + 25$

   b $6a^2 - 16a + 10$

   c $9a^2 + 25$

   d $9a^2 - 30a + 25$

   e None of these

To multiply two expressions, such as $(4x - 3)(5x + 2)$, use the FOIL (First, Outer, Inner, Last) method.

$$(4x - 3)(5x + 2)$$

$$= 20x^2 + 8x - 15x - 6$$
$$= 20x^2 - 7x - 6$$

For Numbers 11 through 14, write your answers.

11. $(5^2)^4 = $ _____

12. $12z - 3(z - 6) = $ _____

13. $(x - 2)(x - 8) = $ _____

14. $\dfrac{15a^2 - 12a}{3a} = $ _____

Reminder

An expression such as $\frac{9x + 6}{3}$ can be written as $\frac{9x}{3} + \frac{6}{3}$ and then simplified, as shown below.

$$\frac{^3 9x}{3^1} + \frac{^2 6}{3^1} = 3x + 2$$

NOTES

NUMBER AND NUMBER OPERATIONS

Number and number operations involves understanding the properties of a number system, and how numbers in the system may be represented and used.

Number and Number Operations includes subskills, such as Equivalent Forms, Percent, Ratio, Proportion, Exponents, and Scientific Notation.

Look at these examples of number and number operations. Choose your answer for each problem.

EXAMPLE	ANSWER
What is 2.05×10^6 written in standard notation? *a* 205,000 *b* 250,000 *c* 2,050,000 *d* 2,500,000	• **Answer *a* is not** correct. This number is the standard notation for 2.05×10^5. • **Answer *b* is not** correct. This number is the standard notation for 2.5×10^5. • **Answer *c* is** correct. Since $10^6 = 1,000,000$, then $2.05 \times 10^6 = 2,050,000$. • **Answer *d* is not** correct. This number is the standard notation for 2.5×10^6.

EXAMPLE	ANSWER

A motorboat used 2.5 gallons of fuel to travel 12 miles. At this rate, how much fuel would it use to travel 30 miles?

a 5 gallons

b 6.25 gallons

c 20.5 gallons

d 144 gallons

- **Answer a** is **not** correct. Since 2.5 gallons were used to travel 12 miles, 5 gallons would only be enough fuel to travel 24 miles.

- **Answer b** is correct. The problem can be solved using a proportion, as shown below.

$$\frac{2.5}{12} = \frac{x}{30}$$

$$12x = 75$$

$$x = 6.25$$

- **Answer c** is **not** correct. The difference between 30 miles and 12 miles was added to the number of gallons used to travel 12 miles.

- **Answer d** is **not** correct. This is the result of solving the following incorrect proportion.

$$\frac{2.5}{12} = \frac{30}{x}$$

Do these number and number operations problems.
First, try Numbers 1 and 2 for practice.

1. Which of these numbers is thirty-three thousandths?

   a 0.33

   b 0.033

   c 0.0033

   d 0.00033

   ANSWER **b** is correct. The third place value to the right of the decimal point is *thousandths*. Since 0.001 is one thousandth, then 0.033 is thirty-three thousandths.

2. Mark has a stack of 50 dishes to wash. It took him 2 minutes to wash 8 dishes. At this rate, how long will it take Mark to wash 50 dishes?

   a   7.5 minutes

   b   9 minutes

   c   12.5 minutes

   d   15 minutes

   ANSWER **c** is correct. The problem can be solved using the proportion $\frac{x}{50} = \frac{2}{8}$, where x equals the number of minutes it will take to wash 50 dishes.

$$\frac{x}{50} = \frac{2}{8}; \; 8x = 100; \; \frac{8x}{8} = \frac{100}{8}; \; x = 12.5$$

Now you are ready to do more problems. The answers to the problems in this section can be found in the back of this workbook.

You use number and number operations when you convert a fraction to a percent. For example, if your daughter makes 9 out of 15 basket attempts in a basketball game, you can tell her she's shooting 60%.

3. What number comes next in the sequence shown below?

0.7, 1.4, 2.1, 2.8, 3.5, _____

a 3.7

b 3.8

c 4.1

d 4.2

Some number sequences are formed by adding, subtracting, multiplying, or dividing. For example, the sequence 2, 5, 8, 11, 14, . . . is formed by repeatedly adding 3.

Reminder

The ratio of a circle's circumference to its diameter is a constant number represented by the Greek letter π, or pi. Three common approximations of π are shown in the table to the right. Study the table. Then do Numbers 4 and 5.

Approximations of π
3.14
3.1416
$\frac{22}{7}$

4. What is $\frac{22}{7}$ written as a mixed number?

   a $3\frac{1}{7}$

   b $3\frac{3}{7}$

   c $7\frac{1}{3}$

   d $7\frac{2}{3}$

Tip

To rewrite an improper fraction as a mixed number, divide the numerator by the denominator. The quotient becomes a whole number, and the remainder becomes the numerator of a fraction. For example, to rewrite $\frac{19}{8}$ as a mixed number, divide 19 by 8 to get $2\frac{3}{8}$.

5. Which of these is the written form of 3.14?

    a   three and fourteen tenths

    b   three and fourteen hundredths

    c   three and fourteen thousandths

    d   three and fourteen ten-thousandths

To find the percent by which an amount has increased, divide the amount of increase by the original amount. Then convert the decimal into a percent. For example, if the price of gasoline increases from $1.60 to $2.00 per gallon, then this is an increase of $0.40. Since $0.40 ÷ $1.60 = 0.25, the percent increase is 25%.

Tip

A sample of registered state voters was polled to find out how many were in favor of four propositions on a ballot. The table below shows the results of the poll. Study the table. Then do Numbers 6 through 10.

Poll of Registered Voters

Proposition	Percent In Favor				
	Ages 18–29	Ages 30–44	Ages 45–64	Ages 65 and over	Overall
1	29%	30%	32%	33%	31%
2	69%	61%	53%	45%	57%
3	86%	88%	85%	89%	87%
4	56%	52%	48%	48%	51%

6. There were 1,000 voters polled in all. How many of them were in favor of Proposition 1?

   a   3.1

   b   31

   c   310

   d 3,100

7. For each proposition, there were 250 voters polled in each age group. How many **more** voters aged 18–29 were in favor of Proposition 3 than Proposition 4?

   a   30

   b   75

   c   140

   d 215

8. For which proposition does the percent in favor change by the same amount from one age group to the next?

   a Proposition 1

   b Proposition 2

   c Proposition 3

   d Proposition 4

9. What fraction of voters ages 30 to 44 were in favor of Proposition 1?

   a $\frac{3}{10}$

   b $\frac{7}{10}$

   c $\frac{3}{100}$

   d $\frac{7}{100}$

10. Which of these decimals represents the percent of voters aged 65 and over who were in favor of Proposition 4?

    a 0.024

    b 0.048

    c 0.24

    d 0.48

11. Approximately 1% of the people who live in a certain city attended a festival. The city population is about 1 million. Approximately how many people attended the festival?

   a   100

   b   1,000

   c   10,000

   d 100,000

12. A wallet is priced at $14.95. Which expression gives the total cost of the wallet, including a 6% sales tax?

   a 1.06($14.95)

   b 1.6($14.95)

   c $14.95 + $0.06

   d $14.95 + $0.60

Reminder

To convert a percent to a decimal, move the decimal point 2 places to the left and drop the percent symbol. For example:

$$6\% = 0.06$$

The table below shows the average traffic level in recent years on a certain freeway. Study the table. Then do Numbers 13 and 14.

Freeway Traffic

Year	Average Traffic Level (in vehicles per minute)
1980	20
1985	30
1990	46
1995	68
2000	101

13. Which of these proportions could be solved to find *L*, the 1995 average traffic level in vehicles per second?

a $\frac{L}{1} = \frac{68}{60}$

b $\frac{L}{1} = \frac{60}{68}$

c $\frac{L}{60} = \frac{68}{1}$

d $\frac{L}{60} = \frac{60}{68}$

14. What was the percent increase in the average traffic level between 1980 and 1985?

a 10%

b 20%

c 50%

d 100%

A chemist made three measurements of the mass of a chemical compound. The table below shows the measurements. Study the table. Then do Numbers 15 and 16.

Mass of Compound

Measurement	Mass (in grams)
1	4.673×10^{-5}
2	4.669×10^{-5}
3	4.671×10^{-5}

15. What is 4.673×10^{-5} written in standard notation?

   a 0.00004673

   b 0.000004673

   c 4.0000673

   d 4.00000673

16. What is 186,000 written in scientific notation?

   a 1.86×10^3

   b 186×10^5

   c 18.6×10^6

   d 1.86×10^5

Reminder

Scientific notation is based on powers of 10. For example, since $10^4 = 10,000$, then $5.3 \times 10^4 = 5.3 \times 10,000 = 53,000$. For small numbers, we use negative exponents.

$$10^{-3} = \frac{1}{10^3} = \frac{1}{1,000} = 0.001$$

$$4.8 \times 10^{-3} = 4.8 \times 0.001 = 0.0048$$

17. Which of these is another way to write 0.025?

    a   25%

    b $\frac{2}{5}$

    c   2.5%

    d $\frac{25}{10,000}$

18. Which of these statements is equivalent to the statement below?

> The square root of *N* is *x*.

    a $2x = N$

    b $x^2 = N$

    c $2N = x$

    d $N^2 = x$

Taking a square root is the inverse of squaring a number. For example, since $5^2 = 5 \times 5 = 25$, we say the square root of 25 (or $\sqrt{25}$) is 5 (or one of its two equal factors). Taking a cube root is the inverse of cubing a number. For example, since $4^3 = 4 \times 4 \times 4 = 64$, we say the cube root of 64 (or $\sqrt[3]{64}$) is 4 (or one of its three equal factors).

Reminder

For Numbers 19 through 24, write your answers.

Read the advertisement below, then do Numbers 19 and 20.

19. What percent discount is represented by the sale price shown in the advertisement?

   _____

20. Leticia left the store with a total of 12 videotapes. How many of them did she get for free?

   _____

21. On a job site where there are 100 laborers, the ratio of skilled to unskilled laborers is 3:7. How many of the laborers are unskilled?

   _____

22. What is $\frac{7}{8}$ written as a decimal?

   _____

23. What is the cube root of 8?

   _____

24. What is 0.004 written in scientific notation?

   _____

COMPUTATION IN CONTEXT

Computation in context is the process of determining the outcome of a variety of real-life problems. We do this using mathematical processes such as addition, subtraction, multiplication, and division.

Computation in Context includes subskills, such as Decimals, Fractions, and Percents.

Look at these examples of computation in context. Choose your answer for each problem.

EXAMPLE	ANSWER
Julie bought $\frac{1}{2}$ pound of Parmesan cheese. She grated $\frac{1}{8}$ pound of the cheese on top of a bowl of pasta. How much of the cheese was left?	• **Answer a** is **not** correct. The subtraction problem was written as $\frac{1}{8} - \frac{1}{2}$ instead of $\frac{1}{2} - \frac{1}{8}$, and the denominators were simply subtracted.
a $\frac{1}{6}$ pound	• **Answer b** is **not** correct. This is the result of the subtraction problem $\frac{1}{2} - \frac{1}{4}$.
b $\frac{1}{4}$ pound	• **Answer c** is correct. To solve $\frac{1}{2} - \frac{1}{8}$, the fraction $\frac{1}{2}$ can be written as $\frac{4}{8}$. When $\frac{1}{8}$ is subtracted from $\frac{4}{8}$, the result is $\frac{3}{8}$.
c $\frac{3}{8}$ pound	
d $\frac{5}{8}$ pound	• **Answer d** is **not** correct. The fractions were added instead of subtracted.

EXAMPLE	ANSWER

A natural cosmetics company donates 5% of its profits to environmental organizations. The company's profit in a year is $15,000,000. How much money will it donate to environmental organizations?

a $75,000

b $300,000

c $750,000

d $3,000,000

- **Answer a** is **not** correct. This is 0.5% of the profit for the year.

- **Answer b** is **not** correct. This is 2% of the profit for the year.

- **Answer c** is correct. The percent can be converted to a decimal, then multiplied by the profit as follows: 5% × $15,000,000 = 0.05 × $15,000,000 = $750,000.

- **Answer d** is **not** correct. The profit for the year was divided by 5 instead of multiplied by 5%.

**Do these computation in context problems.
First, try Numbers 1 and 2 for practice.**

1. An automobile dealer spends $3,000 per month on landscaping. Of this amount, 40% is spent on materials, and the rest is spent on labor. What is the amount spent per month on materials?

    a　　$75

    b　　$120

    c　　$1,200

    d　　$1,800

    ANSWER *c* is correct. The total cost must be multiplied by 40%, or 0.4, giving a result of $1,200.

Computation in context is used whenever a grocery bill is added up, checkbook amounts are subtracted, a price is multiplied by a percentage discount, or the number of students in a class is divided by the number of cars available for a field trip.

2. To make a pair of earrings, a jeweler is using silver wire with a thickness of 0.038 centimeter, and copper wire with a thickness of 0.1 centimeter. How much thicker is the copper wire than the silver wire?

a 0.028 cm

b 0.048 cm

c 0.062 cm

d 0.072 cm

ANSWER *c* is correct. It helps to write 0.1 as 0.100 before subtracting 0.038.

$$\begin{array}{r} 0.100 \\ -\ 0.038 \\ \hline 0.062 \end{array}$$

Now you are ready to do more problems. The answers to the problems in this section can be found in the back of this workbook.

Nate is a truck driver. The table below gives information about the truck he owns and operates. Study the table. Then do Numbers 3 through 6.

Truck Information

Weight	8,300 pounds
Total length	48 feet
Maximum load capacity	6,400 pounds
Fuel tank capacity	150 gallons
Fuel mileage	4.5 miles per gallon

3. Since 1 ton = 2,000 pounds, what is the weight, in tons, of Nate's truck?

 a 4.15 tons

 b 4.3 tons

 c 6.3 tons

 d 7.35 tons

4. When Nate first purchased the truck, the fuel mileage was 5.0 miles per gallon. By what percent has the fuel mileage decreased since then?

 a 0.5%

 b 1.0%

 c 5%

 d 10%

5. The cab of the truck is $\frac{1}{3}$ as long as the box. The cab and the box together make up the total length of the truck. How long is the box?

    a 12 feet

    b 16 feet

    c 32 feet

    d 36 feet

6. According to the information given in the chart, how far can the truck travel on one tank of fuel?

    a 625 miles

    b 650 miles

    c 675 miles

    d 750 miles

The chart below shows a factory outlet store's cost per unit for some articles of clothing and the percent markup that will be added to the cost. Study the chart. Then do Numbers 7 through 10.

Cost and Markup

Article of Clothing	Store's Cost	Markup
Tie	$12.50	10%
Shirt	$20.00	20%
Pair of slacks	$50.00	30%
Suit	$275.00	20%

7. What is the selling price of each shirt at the factory outlet store?

   a $20

   b $22

   c $24

   d $26

8. If the store sells 100 pairs of slacks, how much of the total money it receives for the slacks is markup?

   a $150

   b $1,500

   c $5,000

   d $6,500

9. The factory outlet store is selling everything at the store's cost during a special sale. Which of these would cost exactly $175?

   a 8 shirts and 1 tie

   b 7 shirts and 4 ties

   c 5 shirts and 6 ties

   d 4 shirts and 8 ties

10. During the special sale, a customer bought a tie and suit at the store's cost. How much did the customer save compared to the markup price?

   a $56.25

   b $68.75

   c $287.50

   d $343.75

For Numbers 11 through 15, write your answers.

11. The regular price of a sewing machine is $88. It is on sale at a discount of 15%. What is the sale price?

_____

The table below shows the hourly pay rates of nurses at a certain hospital. Study the table. Then do Numbers 12 through 15.

Pay Rates of Nurses

Type of Nurse	Hourly Rate
Certified Nursing Assistant (CNA)	$9.00
Licensed Vocational Nurse (LVN)	$16.00
Registered Nurse (RN)	$24.00

12. The overtime pay rate is determined by multiplying the regular hourly rate by 1.5. What is the overtime pay rate for a CNA?

_____

13. Liz is an RN. She can multiply her pay rate by 0.075 to calculate the amount of money she is contributing to her retirement plan for each hour of work. What amount is Liz contributing per hour?

_____

When multiplying decimals, add the number of decimal places in the two factors. That tells you how many decimal places will be in the answer. For example:

$$35.\underline{7} \times 0.\underline{073} = 2.\underline{6061}$$

14. If an LVN works 35 hours per week at the regular hourly rate, what are his or her total weekly earnings?

   _____

15. Melinda is an RN and her husband Tim is an LVN. Together, they work a total of 50 hours per week, and each earns the same amount per week. How many hours per week does Tim work?

   _____

ESTIMATION

Estimation is the process of finding an approximate answer rather than an exact answer to a calculation. When an exact answer is not needed, it is often quicker and easier to use an estimate.

Estimation includes subskills, such as Estimation, Rounding, and Reasonableness of Answer.

Look at these examples of estimation. Choose your answer for each problem.

EXAMPLE	ANSWER

EXAMPLE

Which of these is the best estimate of $689 \div 0.48$?

a   300

b   350

c   1,200

d   1,400

ANSWER

- **Answer a** is **not** correct. The number 689 was rounded to 600 instead of 700, then multiplied by 0.5 instead of divided.

- **Answer b** is **not** correct. The number 689 was rounded to 700, but multiplied by 0.5 instead of divided.

- **Answer c** is **not** correct. The number 689 was rounded to 600 instead of 700, then divided by 0.5.

- **Answer d** is correct. The number 689 can be rounded to 700, then divided by 0.5.

EXAMPLE	ANSWER

The number of apartments available in a city has decreased from 602 last year to 511 this year. Which of these is the best estimate of the percent of this decrease?

a   5%

b   10%

c   15%

d   20%

- **Answer *a*** is **not** correct. The decrease in the number of apartments is about 90, while 5% of 602 is only about 30.

- **Answer *b*** is **not** correct. The decrease in the number of apartments is about 90, while 10% of 602 is only about 60.

- **Answer *c*** is correct. The decrease in the number of apartments is about 90, which is about 15% of 602.

- **Answer *d*** is **not** correct. This would be a decrease of about 120 apartments, which is greater than the actual decrease reported in the problem.

Do these estimation problems.
First, try Numbers 1 and 2 for practice.

1. Carmen and Ted went to a restaurant for lunch. Their total bill was $24.80. If they tipped the waiter 15% of the bill, which of these is the best estimate of the amount of the tip?

   a less than $2.50

   b between $2.50 and $3.50

   c between $3.50 and $4.50

   d more than $4.50

   ANSWER *c* is correct. Since the bill was about $25, then 15% of $25 is $0.15 \times \$25 = \$3.75$.

2. A family traveled about 185 miles each day on a 5-day trip. Their van averaged 17 miles per gallon during the trip. Which of these is closest to the total number of gallons of gasoline used?

   a 25

   b 50

   c 75

   d 100

   ANSWER *b* is correct. Since 185 is close to 200, and 17 is close to 20, the approximate number of gallons used per day is $200 \div 20 = 10$. The approximate total used for 5 days is: $5 \times 10 = 50$ gallons.

Now you are ready to do more problems. The answers to the problems in this section can be found in the back of this workbook.

The table below shows the amount of water used for different purposes in a certain county last year. Study the table. Then do Numbers 3 through 6.

Water Usage

Type of Use	Usage (in acre-feet)
Residential	387,485
Industrial	966,079
Agricultural	4,220,832
Total	**5,574,396**

3. Which of these percents is the best estimate of the amount of water that was used for industrial purposes?

a less than 10%

b between 10% and 15%

c between 15% and 20%

d more than 20%

In many situations an exact amount is not needed, but an estimate is helpful. A person may say, "There were about 100 people watching the soccer game," or "Buy about 2 pounds of beans," or "Dinner will cost about $8.00 per person." These are all examples of estimates.

Chicken Dinner
$7.98 per person

4. The amount of water used for agriculture is about what fractional part of the total amount of water used?

a $\frac{2}{3}$

b $\frac{4}{5}$

c $\frac{7}{8}$

d $\frac{9}{10}$

5. What is the amount of residential water usage rounded to the nearest hundred acre-feet?

a 387,000

b 387,400

c 387,490

d 387,500

Reminder

If an exact answer to a computation problem is not needed, round the numbers before doing the computation. The result will be an estimate of the actual answer.

6. What is the amount of total water usage rounded to the nearest ten thousand acre-feet?

   a 5,570,000

   b 5,574,000

   c 5,600,000

   d 6,000,000

To estimate a percentage of an amount, begin by rounding the percent and/or the amount. Then convert the percent to a decimal and multiply. For example, to estimate 17% of 315: Round 17% up to 20%. Then round 315 down to 300 and multiply. $0.2 \times 300 = 60$

Cheryl works for a small nonprofit agency. The circle graph below shows the agency's total budget allocated for various purposes. Study the circle graph. Then do Numbers 7 and 8.

Budget Allocations

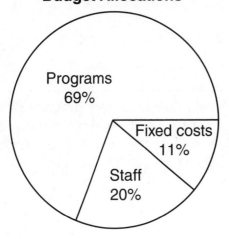

7. Which of these is the best estimate of the fraction of the budget allocated for fixed costs?

   a $\frac{1}{6}$

   b $\frac{1}{10}$

   c $\frac{1}{14}$

   d $\frac{1}{16}$

8. If the total annual budget is $331,500, which of these is the best estimate of the amount of money allocated to programs?

   a $180,000

   b $230,000

   c $250,000

   d $275,000

9. Which of these is the best estimate of 1.52 ÷ 4.87?

   a 0.2

   b 0.3

   c 0.02

   d 0.03

10. Vanessa spends about $73 every time she shops for groceries. If she buys groceries about 6 times every 4 months, which of these amounts is closest to how much Vanessa spends on groceries in one year?

   a less than $500

   b between $500 and $1,000

   c between $1,000 and $1,500

   d more than $1,500

One way to estimate a number is to use front end estimation. For example, 772 rounds to 700 using front-end estimation. But to estimate a computation involving a number, it is better to round the number to the nearest 10 or 100. For example, for the problem 772 × 3, a better estimate is given by 800 × 3 than by 700 × 3.

11. Which of these is the best estimate of the amount of the rectangle that is shaded?

a $\frac{3}{4}$

b 0.50

c $\frac{2}{3}$

d 88%

12. If $\overline{AB}$ represents 10 units, which of these is the best estimate of the total distance around figure MNOP?

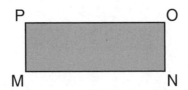

a 20 units

b 40 units

c 60 units

d 80 units

For Numbers 13 through 16, write your answers.

13. What is 16.6429 rounded to the nearest thousandth?

_____

14. Daniel rounded the number below to the nearest hundredth. Irena rounded the number to the nearest tenth. What was the difference between their answers?

| 0.84167 |

_____

To round a number to a place value, look at the digit to the right of the place value. If that digit is less than 5, round down. If it is 5 or greater, round up. For example: When rounding 29.63 to the nearest tenth, since the digit to the right of the tenths place is a 3, round down to 29.60. When rounding 2.75 to the nearest tenth, since the digit to the right of the tenths place is a 5, round up to 2.80.

The chart below gives information about three different checking accounts available at a bank. Study the chart. Then do Numbers 15 and 16.

Checking Accounts

Plan	Monthly Fee	Per-Check Fee
Basic Checking	$5.00 per month	$0.15 per check
Standard Checking	$7.50 per month	First 20 checks per month are free; then $0.15 per check
Platinum Checking	$10.00 per month	Unlimited free checks

15. Sharon's account is Basic Checking. Last month, she wrote 28 checks. To the nearest dollar, what is the best estimate of the total fees Sharon paid for the month?

_____

16. Rick's account is Standard Checking. Last month, he wrote 47 checks. To the nearest dollar, what is the best estimate of the total fees Rick paid for the month?

_____

NOTES

MEASUREMENT

Measurement involves the use of tools such as rulers, scales, thermometers, and clocks to find information. These tools are marked off in units that allow us to measure length, width, height, weight, temperature, and time. There are two measurement systems commonly used in the United States—the metric system (meters, grams, etc.) and the customary system (feet, pounds, etc.).

Measurement includes subskills, such as Area, Rate, Convert Measurement Units, and Volume.

Look at these examples of measurement. Choose your answer for each problem.

EXAMPLE	ANSWER

A school board meeting began at 7:25 pm and lasted for 2 hours and 48 minutes. At what time did the meeting end?

a   9:03 P.M.

b   9:13 P.M.

c   10:03 P.M.

d   10:13 P.M.

- **Answer a** is **not** correct. The numbers 25 and 48 were added incorrectly for a sum of 63, and the extra hour was not carried to the hours column.

- **Answer b** is **not** correct. The extra hour was not carried to the hours column.

- **Answer c** is **not** correct. The numbers 25 and 48 were, again, added incorrectly for a sum of 63.

- **Answer d** is correct. The sum of 25 and 48 is 73, which when converted to minutes equals 1 hour and 13 minutes. If 2 hours are added to 7:00 P.M., the result is 9:00 P.M., and when the additional hour and 13 minutes is added, the answer is 10:13 P.M.

EXAMPLE	ANSWER

Miguel is using a map drawn to the scale of 1 inch = 5 miles. He plans to ride his bicycle between two towns that are 6.5 inches apart on the map. How far does Miguel plan to ride?

a   1.3 miles

b   11.5 miles

c   30.5 miles

d   32.5 miles

- **Answer *a* is not** correct. The number 6.5 was divided by 5 instead of multiplied by 5.

- **Answer *b* is not** correct. The numbers 5 and 6.5 were added instead of multiplied.

- **Answer *c* is not** correct. The multiplication problem 6.5×5 was done incorrectly.

- **Answer *d* is correct.** Since 1 inch = 5 miles, 6.5 inches = $6.5 \times 5 = 32.5$ miles.

Do these measurement problems.
First, try Numbers 1 and 2 for practice.

1. A patient in a hospital must receive 30 milliliters of glucose each hour. How many **liters** of glucose will the patient receive in 24 hours?

   a   720 liters

   b   72.0 liters

   c   7.20 liters

   d   0.72 liter

   ANSWER *d* is correct. The patient will receive (30 × 24) or 720 milliliters. Since 1 liter = 1,000 milliliters, 720 milliliters divided by 1,000 will convert the milliliters to liters.

   $\frac{720}{1,000} = 0.72$ liter

2. A rectangular prism is 5 centimeters wide, 10 centimeters long, and 4 centimeters high. What is the volume of the prism?

   a   40 cubic centimeters

   b   60 cubic centimeters

   c   200 cubic centimeters

   d   250 cubic centimeters

   ANSWER *c* is correct. The volume is 5 × 10 × 4 = 200 cubic centimeters.

Now you are ready to do more problems. The answers to the problems in this section can be found in the back of this workbook.

The chart and diagram below give information about a new freezer. Study the chart and diagram. Then do Numbers 3 and 4.

FREEZER MODEL 360B
INFORMATION

Outside dimensions:	72" x 36" x 30"
Inside dimensions:	60" x 24" x 18"
Weight:	240 lbs.
Temperature range:	−10°F to 32°F
Regular price:	$799

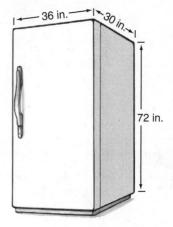

3. The difference between the outside and inside dimensions of the freezer is due to the thickness of the freezer's walls, which is the same on each side of the freezer. What is the thickness of each wall?

   a 3 inches

   b 6 inches

   c 9 inches

   d 12 inches

4. What is the capacity of the inside of the freezer in cubic feet?

   a 15 cubic feet

   b 18 cubic feet

   c 30 cubic feet

   d 45 cubic feet

To find the volume of a rectangular prism, multiply the length, width, and height (*V=lwh*). The answer will be in cubic units.

Reminder

5. Charlotte's average speed in an 18-mile race was 8 miles per hour. If the race started at 9:00 A.M., when did she finish the race?

a   11:15 A.M.

b   11:20 A.M.

c   11:25 A.M.

d   11:30 A.M.

Apply

Knowing how to measure is one of the most useful math skills you will ever learn. It can help you find out the weight of a package you want to mail, the size of a room you want to paint, or even how many miles you have run around a track.

6. Sam took a direct flight from Boston to Los Angeles. The flight left Boston at 2:40 P.M. and lasted 5 hours and 12 minutes. What time was it in Los Angeles when he landed?

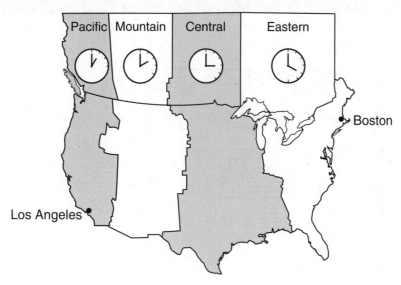

a   4:52 P.M.

b   5:12 P.M.

c   7:52 P.M.

d   10:52 P.M.

7. At 5:00 A.M., the temperature was ⁻5°C. By 7:00 A.M., the temperature was 0°C. If it continued to increase at this rate, what was the temperature at 11:00 A.M.?

a   10°C

b   15°C

c   20°C

d   25°C

Sara is helping to build a square wooden deck around a circular swimming pool 8 meters in diameter. The diagram below shows the plan for the deck. Study the diagram. Then do Numbers 8 through 11.

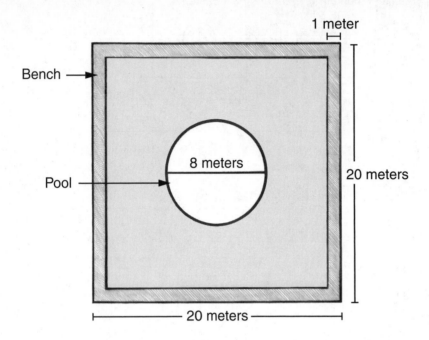

8. A bench 1 meter wide will be built along all four edges of the deck, as shown in the diagram. What will be the total length of the inside edges of the bench?

    a 72 meters

    b 76 meters

    c 78 meters

    d 79 meters

To find the perimeter of a rectangle, add the lengths of the four sides. You can also use the formula $P = 2l + 2w$, where l = length and w = width. To find the area of a rectangle, multiply the length by the width. (The formula is $A = lw$.) The answer will be in square units.

9. Sara is building a section of the bench that will be 20 meters long. She started at 8:00 A.M., and by 9:20 A.M. she has finished a 5-meter section. If she continues at this rate, at what time will she finish the 20-meter section?

    a   10:40 A.M.

    b   12:00 P.M.

    c   1:20 P.M.

    d   2:40 P.M.

10. What will be the approximate area of the deck, including the bench, but not including the pool? (Area of circle = πr^2) (Use 3.14 for π.)

    a   200 square meters

    b   250 square meters

    c   300 square meters

    d   350 square meters

The area formula for a square with side length s is $A = s^2$.

Reminder

11. Sara is earning $8 per hour for the first 8 hours of any day, and $12 per hour for any additional hours in that day. How much money will she earn for working 10 hours in one day?

a $64

b $76

c $88

d $96

This rectangular water tank is 10 feet long, 3 feet wide, and 4 feet deep.

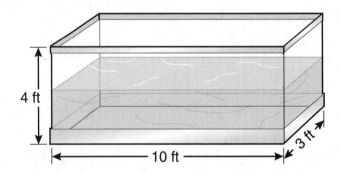

4 ft

10 ft

3 ft

12. How many cubic feet of water does the tank hold when it is full?

a   34 cubic feet

b   52 cubic feet

c   104 cubic feet

d   120 cubic feet

For Numbers 13 through 16, write your answers.

13. Kevin is running a 10-kilometer race. He has run 9.5 kilometers so far. How many **meters** does Kevin have left to run?

_____

14. What is the volume of a cube measuring 10 feet on each edge?

_____

15. The perimeter of a rectangle is 60 feet. The length of one side of the rectangle is 10 feet. What is the area of the rectangle?

_____

16. In the diagram below, ABCD is a rectangle. What is the area of △BCD?

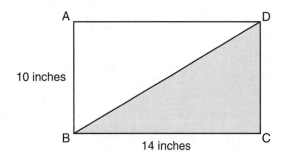

_____

There are 100 centimeters in 1 meter, and 1,000 meters in 1 kilometer.

Reminder

GEOMETRY AND SPATIAL SENSE

Geometry and spatial sense involves determining the relationships, properties, and measurements of all types of shapes, points, lines, angles, plane figures, and solid figures.

Geometry and Spatial Sense includes subskills, such as Plane Figure, Angles, Point, Ray, Line, Plane, and Pythagorean Theorem.

Look at these examples of geometry and spatial sense. Choose your answer for each problem.

EXAMPLE	ANSWER

In the diagram below, lines *x* and *y* are perpendicular, and m∠1 = m∠2 = m∠3. What is the measure of ∠1 ?

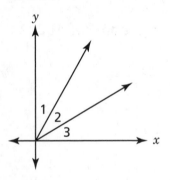

- **a**   15°
- **b**   30°
- **c**   45°
- **d**   60°

- **Answer a** is **not** correct. This would be the correct answer if the angle formed by a pair of perpendicular lines was 45°.

- **Answer b** is correct. The angle formed by a pair of perpendicular lines is a right angle, which measures 90°. Since this right angle is divided into 3 congruent angles, each one has a measure of 30°.

- **Answer c** is **not** correct. This is the result of dividing 90° by 2 instead of by 3.

- **Answer d** is **not** correct. This would be the correct answer if the angle formed by a pair of perpendicular lines were 180°.

EXAMPLE	ANSWER

Which of the these statements is true?

a The diagonals of a rectangle are never perpendicular.

b The diagonals of a rectangle are always perpendicular.

c The diagonals of a rectangle are never the same length.

d The diagonals of a rectangle are always the same length.

- **Answer *a*** is **not** correct. The diagonals of a rectangle are perpendicular if the rectangle is a square.

- **Answer *b*** is **not** correct. If a rectangle is not a square, its diagonals are not perpendicular.

- **Answer *c*** is **not** correct. In any rectangle, the diagonals are the same length.

- **Answer *d*** is correct. In any rectangle, the diagonals are always the same length.

**Do these geometry and spatial sense problems.
First, try Numbers 1 and 2 for practice.**

1. Which of these is similar, but not congruent, to the triangle shown to the right?

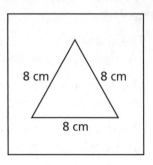

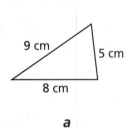

a

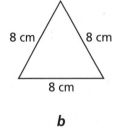

b

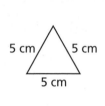

c

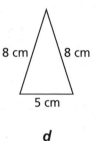

d

ANSWER **c** is correct. The side lengths of this triangle are proportional to the side lengths of the triangle above, but the two triangles are not congruent.

2. What is the length of $\overline{BD}$ in rectangle ABCD?

   a 10 meters

   b 14 meters

   c $2\sqrt{7}$ meters

   d $4\sqrt{3}$ meters

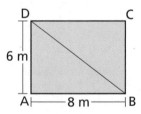

ANSWER **a** is correct. We can use the Pythagorean theorem ($a^2 + b^2 = c^2$).

$$\overline{BD}^2 = 6^2 + 8^2, \ \overline{BD}^2 = 36 + 64, \ \overline{BD}^2 = 100, \ \overline{BD} = 10$$

Now you are ready to do more problems. The answers to the problems in this section can be found in the back of this workbook.

3. How many points are contained in a line?

   a exactly 1

   b exactly 2

   c exactly 4

   d an infinite number

4. Which of these line segments is perpendicular to plane EFGH of the cube?

   a $\overline{HG}$

   b $\overline{HC}$

   c $\overline{AB}$

   d $\overline{AE}$

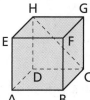

5. Which of these describes figure ACDE?

   a triangle

   b quadrilateral

   c pentagon

   d hexagon

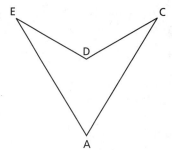

 Geometry terms are used to say things such as "The driveway meets the street at a right angle." Geometry can also be used to figure out distances that are difficult to measure, such as the length and width of a yard or even the height of a building.

The diagram below shows a circle with its center at the origin. Study the diagram. Then do Numbers 6 through 8.

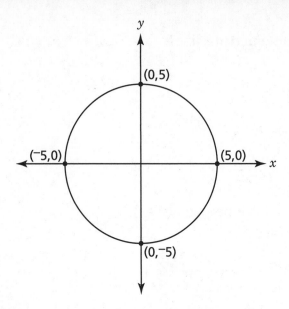

6. Which of these best describes the circle?

a   the set of points exactly 5 units from the origin

b   the set of points less than 5 units from the origin

c   the set of points exactly 10 units from the origin

d   the set of points less than 10 units from the origin

7. Which of these points is inside the circle?

    a (3, ⁻5)

    b (3, 3)

    c (5, ⁻5)

    d (5, 3)

8. What is the length of the diameter of the circle?

    a ⁻5 units

    b 0 units

    c 5 units

    d 10 units

The radius is the distance from the center of a circle to any point on the circle. The diameter is a line segment that passes through the center of the circle and has its end points on the circle. The diameter equals twice the distance of the radius.

Reminder

In the diagram below, angles 1 through 10 each have the same measure. Study the diagram. Then do Number 9.

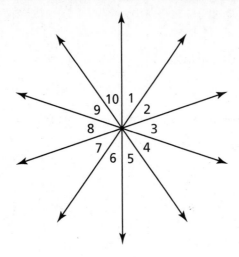

9. What is the measure of ∠1?

   a 18°

   b 30°

   c 36°

   d 40°

Reminder

A circle has 360°.

10. Which of these figures is **not** possible?

   a a triangle with exactly one right angle

   b a triangle with exactly two right angles

   c a quadrilateral with exactly one right angle

   d a quadrilateral with exactly two right angles

11. Which of these best represents the side view of the cylinder shown below?

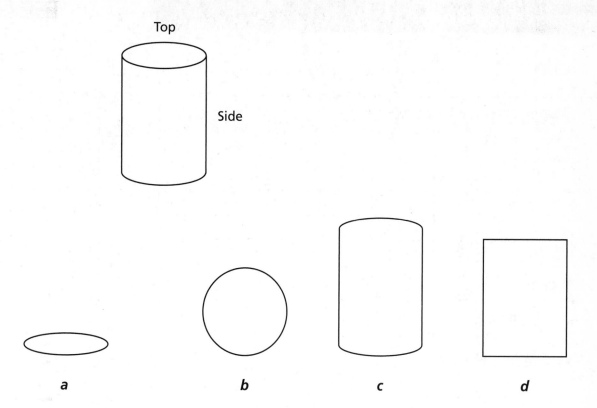

Top

Side

a   b   c   d

12. Which set of dimensions below is similar to a rectangle with the dimensions 2 feet by 8 feet?

a   4 feet by 16 feet

b   6 feet by 12 feet

c   12 feet by 32 feet

d   22 feet by 28 feet

A park ranger is using this topographical map to pinpoint the location of a small forest fire. Study the map. Then do Numbers 13 through 15.

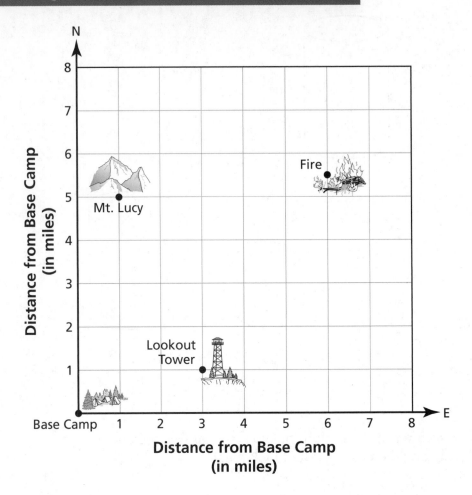

13. Which of these best describes the location of the fire on the grid?

    a   (5.5, 6)

    b   (6.5, 5)

    c   (6, 5.5)

    d   (6, 6.5)

In an ordered pair, the *x*-coordinate (or horizontal coordinate) is listed first. For example, the ordered pair (2, 5) describes the point 2 units to the right and 5 units up from the origin.

Reminder

14. Which of these diagrams best represents the placement of the Lookout Tower, Mt. Lucy, and the forest fire as seen, without depth perception, from Base Camp?

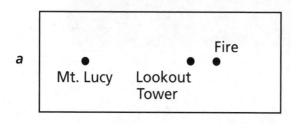

a

Fire

Mt. Lucy   Lookout
Tower

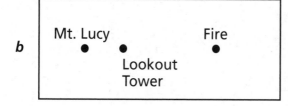

b

Mt. Lucy   Fire

Lookout
Tower

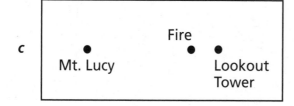

c

Fire

Mt. Lucy   Lookout
Tower

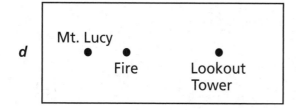

d

Mt. Lucy

Fire   Lookout
Tower

15. Which of these represents the straight-line distance from the Lookout Tower to the forest fire?

a   7.5 miles

b $\sqrt{7.5}$ miles

c $3^2 + 4.5^2$ miles

d $\sqrt{3^2 + 4.5^2}$ miles

The diagram below shows the designs for two sails on a sailboat. In the diagram, △ABE is similar to △CBD; $\overline{AB}$ = 6 feet, $\overline{BC}$ = 9 feet, $\overline{CD}$ = 15 feet, and $\overline{BD}$ is perpendicular to $\overline{AC}$. Study the diagram. Then do Numbers 16 through 19, and write your answers.

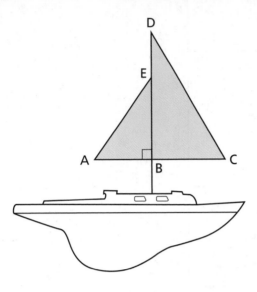

16. What geometric term best describes $\overline{CD}$?

_____

17. What is the length of $\overline{AE}$?

_____

18. What is the length of $\overline{BD}$?

_____

19. If the measure of $\angle BDC$ is 37°, what is the measure of $\angle BCD$?

_____

The measure of a right angle is 90°. The sum of the measure of the angles in a triangle is 180°.

Reminder

DATA ANALYSIS

Data are numerical facts displayed in the form of graphs, charts, tables, or diagrams. *Data analysis* is the process of acquiring information or meaning from the data.

Data Analysis includes subskills, such as Bar, Line, Circle Graph, and Conclusions from Data.

Look at these examples of data analysis. Choose your answer for each problem.

| EXAMPLE | ANSWER |

The table below shows the average number of customers per day at four grocery stores. Study the table.

Grocery Store Customers

Store	Average Number of Customers (per day)
Big Deal	920
Only Natural	280
Happy's	630
Food Cheap	1,250

Which store has about 20% of the total number of customers of all four stores?

a Big Deal

b Only Natural

c Happy's

d Food Cheap

- **Answer a** is **not** correct. There are a total of 3,080 customers, so 920 is about 30% of the total.

- **Answer b** is **not** correct. Only Natural has about 10% of the total.

- **Answer c** is correct. Happy's has 630 customers, which is about 20% of 3,080.

- **Answer d** is **not** correct. Food Cheap has about 40% of the total.

EXAMPLE	ANSWER

The bar graph below shows the estimated population of three types of fish in a lake. Study the graph.

Fish Population

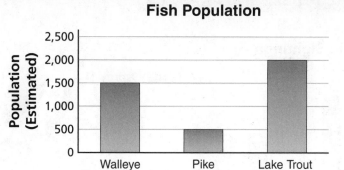

Type of Fish

About what fraction of the fish in the lake are pike?

a $\frac{1}{8}$

b $\frac{1}{6}$

c $\frac{1}{4}$

d $\frac{1}{3}$

- **Answer a** is correct. There are about 500 pike, and the total number of fish in the lake is about 4,000. Therefore, the fraction is $\frac{500}{4,000}$, which reduces to $\frac{1}{8}$.

- **Answer b** is **not** correct. This would be correct if the total number of fish were 3,000 instead of 4,000.

- **Answer c** is **not** correct. This would be correct if the total number of fish were 2,000 instead of 4,000.

- **Answer d** is **not** correct. This would be correct if each type of fish had the same population.

Do these data analysis problems.
First, try Numbers 1 and 2 for practice.

The graph below shows the results of a 4-day bird watch.
Use this graph to answer Numbers 1 and 2.

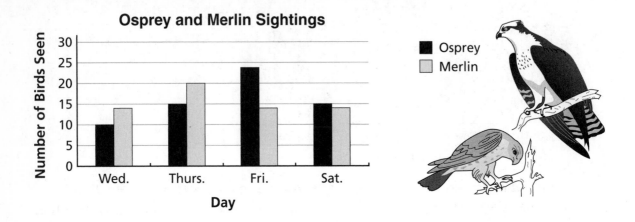

1. What day had the greatest total number of osprey and merlin sightings?

   a Wednesday

   b Thursday

   c Friday

   d Saturday

ANSWER *c* is correct. There were 24 ospreys and 13 merlins sighted on Friday, making a total of 37 birds. This total is greater than the total on any other day.

2. What is the median number of ospreys seen on the 4-day bird watch?

  a 14

  b 15

  c 16

  d 17

ANSWER *b* is correct. The number of ospreys seen on each of the four days is as follows: 10, 15, 24, and 15. If the numbers are put in numerical order, they are 10, 15, 15, and 24. The two middle values are 15 and 15, and their average is 15.

> **Now you are ready to do more problems. The answers to the problems in this section can be found in the back of this workbook.**

The circle graph below shows how the budget for a large construction project will be spent. Study the graph. Then do Numbers 3 through 5.

Project Costs

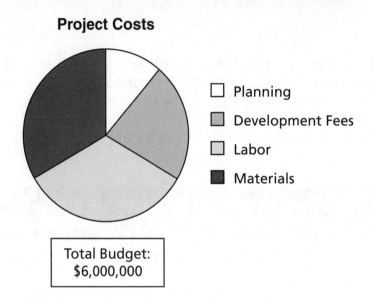

☐ Planning
☐ Development Fees
☐ Labor
☐ Materials

Total Budget:
$6,000,000

3. The total budget for the project is $6,000,000. About how much money will be spent on labor?

a $1,500,000

b $2,000,000

c $3,000,000

d $4,500,000

Reminder

In a circle graph, each section represents a fraction or percentage of the total. All the sections must add up to one whole, or 100%.

You might say that data analysis tells "the real story behind the numbers." If a newspaper story shows a graph which displays how the price of gas has risen over the past year, data analysis helps you figure out exactly how much the price has changed.

4. Which of these is a true statement about the graph?

   a   The materials expense will be about 3 times the planning expense.

   b   The labor expense will be more than 2 times the development fees.

   c   The materials expense will be $500,000 greater than the labor expense.

   d   The development fees will be over $2,000,000.

5. About what percent of the budget will be spent on materials and labor combined?

   a   60%

   b   70%

   c   80%

   d   90%

To estimate the percentage represented by a section of a circle graph, use the basic fractional equivalents as guidelines. For example:

$$\frac{1}{4} = 25\%, \frac{1}{2} = 50\%, \text{ and } \frac{1}{3} \approx 33\%$$

Two painters are painting a house. The graph below shows their progress throughout one day. Use this graph to do Numbers 6 and 7.

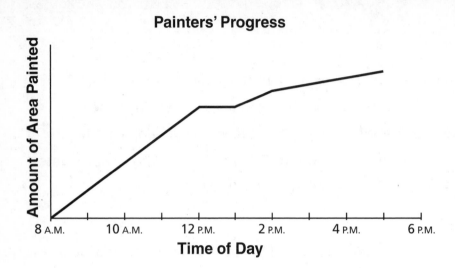

Painters' Progress

6. Which of these is consistent with the graph?

  a Both painters painted continuously from 8 A.M. to 5 P.M.

  b One painter took a lunch break from 12 P.M. to 1 P.M., while the other painter continued painting.

  c Both painters took a lunch break at 12 P.M. and resumed painting at 1 P.M.

  d One painter stopped painting for the day at 12 P.M. The other painter stopped painting for the day at 1 P.M.

7. During which time period does the graph have the greatest rate of increase?

  a 8 A.M. to 12 P.M.

  b 12 P.M. to 1 P.M.

  c 1 P.M. to 2 P.M.

  d 2 P.M. to 5 P.M.

On a line graph, an increase is represented by a line that rises as it moves from left to right.

Reminder

The table below shows the family rates for the Garden Inn.
Study the table. Then do Numbers 8 and 9.

Garden Inn Family Rates

	Sun–Thurs	Fri–Sat
June, July, August	**$65** per night	**$75** per night
All other months	**$55** per night	**$65** per night
8% sales tax charged $0.50 per local telephone call		

8. The McKees stayed at the inn 3 nights in July and made 6 local
   telephone calls. What additional information is needed to determine
   the McKees' total bill?

   a the number of children in the McKee family

   b the amount of sales tax the Garden Inn charges

   c what time of the year the McKees stayed at the inn

   d which three nights of the week the McKees stayed at the inn

To find what additional information is needed to solve
a problem, first try to solve the problem with only
the given information.

9. Jen is considering the following two-night stays at the Garden Inn:

1. Wednesday/Thursday nights in August
2. Friday/Saturday nights in October
3. Thursday/Friday nights in April

Which of these two-night stays will cost the same amount?

a 1 and 2

b 2 and 3

c 1 and 3

d 1, 2, and 3

The chart below shows the rates that four telephone companies charge for long-distance calling card calls. Study the chart. Then do Numbers 10 through 12.

Calling Card Rates

Company	Monthly Fee	First minute of each call	Cost per additional minute
1	$3.50	$0.75	$0.15
2	None	$0.95	$0.15
3	$2.95	$0.25	$0.20
4	None	$1.20	$0.12

10. Susan is a customer of Company 1. In a certain month, she used her card to make 10 telephone calls, each 5 minutes long. What was Susan's total bill for the month?

   a $13.50

   b $17.00

   c $37.50

   d $41.00

11. Terrance makes several calling card calls every day, but each call lasts for 5 minutes or less. Which company should he choose to get the least expensive service?

    a   Company 1

    b   Company 2

    c   Company 3

    d   Company 4

12. Jennifer is a customer of Company 4. One month she used her calling card a total of 8 times, and her bill for the month was $19.44. How many total minutes did Jennifer spend on the telephone for the 8 calls?

    a   15

    b   16

    c   90

    d   162

For Numbers 13 through 16, write your answers.

The advertisement below shows the prices for an all-you-can-eat buffet. Use the advertisement to help you do Numbers 13 through 15.

13. Larry is 41 years old. He usually goes to the dinner buffet at this restaurant at 4:30 P.M., 3 days per week. How much money per week could he save by eating an hour earlier on each visit to the restaurant?

_____

14. The Rono family consists of Diane and Peter, who are in their thirties, and 10-year-old twin girls. How much **more** will it cost the family to have the dinner buffet when the girls reach the age of 11?

   _____

15. What would be the total cost of the dinner buffet for the family listed in the chart?

   _____

The Williams Family

Sue	Age 68
Woody	Age 32
Felicia	Age 30
Laura	Age 6
Max	Age 2

The double line graph below shows the temperature variations at two elevations on a mountain during a 24-hour period. Study the graph. Then do Number 16.

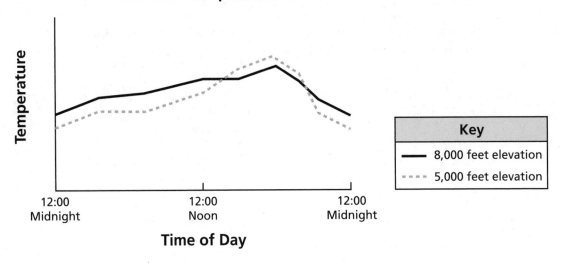

Mountain Temperatures

16. According to the graph, how many times during the 24-hour period was the temperature the same at the two elevations?

_____

NOTES

STATISTICS AND PROBABILITY

Statistics involves the collection, organization, and interpretation of numerical data.

Probability is the likelihood of a certain event occurring, and is expressed as a ratio or a fraction.

Statistics and Probability includes subskills, such as Independent Events, Mean, Mode, Median, Range, and Sampling.

Look at this example of statistics and probability. Choose your answer.

EXAMPLE   ANSWER

The table below shows the high temperatures recorded in a city for one week. Study the table.

Daily High Temperatures

Day	Sun	Mon	Tue	Wed	Thu	Fri	Sat
Temperature	74	75	80	81	75	77	84

Which of these temperatures is the mode for the temperatures recorded in the table?

a 74 degrees

b 75 degrees

c 77 degrees

d 78 degrees

- **Answer *a* is not** correct. This is the lowest temperature recorded that week.

- **Answer *b* is correct.** The mode is the temperature that was recorded the most.

- **Answer *c* is not** correct. This is the median temperature recorded that week.

- **Answer *d* is not** correct. This is the mean temperature recorded that week.

Do these statistics and probability problems.
First, try Numbers 1 and 2 for practice.

1. Roberto has a mixture of colored balloons in a bag that need to be filled with helium. He has 2 brown, 4 blue, 8 black, and 10 gray balloons. He reached into the bag without looking and pulled out a black balloon. What is the probability that the next balloon he pulls out will also be black?

a $\frac{7}{69}$

b $\frac{7}{23}$

c $\frac{1}{9}$

d $\frac{2}{3}$

ANSWER a is correct. The probability of drawing one black balloon is $\frac{8}{24}$, which reduces to $\frac{1}{3}$. Then the probability of drawing another black balloon is now $\frac{7}{23}$. Multiply the two probabilities. $\frac{1}{3} \times \frac{7}{23} = \frac{7}{69}$

> The table below shows the points scored by Debbie for her first 7 basketball games. Study the table. Then do Number 2.

Debbie's Points

Game	1	2	3	4	5	6	7
Points	15	22	12	15	11	10	13

2. What is the mean (average) of the points she scored for the 7 games?

   a 12 points

   b 13 points

   c 14 points

   d 15 points

ANSWER *c* is correct. To find the mean, calculate the sum of the data. Then divide the sum by the number of items.

$$15 + 22 + 12 + 15 + 11 + 10 + 13 = 98$$

$$98 \div 7 = 14$$

> Now you are ready to do more problems. The answers to the problems in this section can be found in the back of this workbook.

The spinner shown below is used for a game at a county fair. Study the spinner. Then do Numbers 3 and 4.

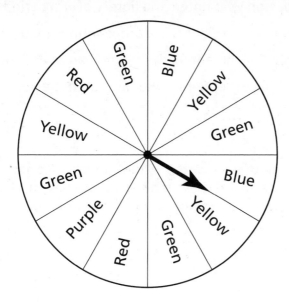

3. On which color is the spinner most likely to stop?

    a red

    b blue

    c green

    d yellow

4. On which two colors does the spinner have an equal chance of stopping?

    a green and yellow

    b blue and red

    c purple and green

    d yellow and red

5. A city council conducted a survey to see if its residents would support a 0.25% increase in the sales tax in order to fund the public library. Which survey would provide the most reliable information?

    a surveying every third person who enters the library over a period of days

    b surveying a random sample of residents in each neighborhood of the city

    c surveying every fifth person who enters the city hall on a random day

    d surveying a random sample of residents who have used the library in the last six months

6. For a picnic, Glen mixed 36 bottles of water, 18 diet drinks, 24 colas, and 12 iced tea drinks into a large ice chest. If a person reaches into the ice chest and pulls out a drink without looking, what is the probability the drink would be a cola?

    a $\frac{1}{90}$

    b $\frac{1}{24}$

    c $\frac{4}{15}$

    d $\frac{4}{11}$

Tip

To find the probability of a certain event occurring, divide the amount of the certain event by the total amount of all possible events. For example:

A cooler contains a mixture of 12 cans of raspberry juice, 10 cans of orange juice, and 18 cans of apple juice. Without looking, what is the probability of selecting a can of orange juice from the cooler?

$$\frac{10}{12 + 10 + 18} = \frac{10}{40} = \frac{1}{4}$$

To create a budget, Linda wanted to determine her average monthly electric bill. She rounded some previous month's bills to the nearest dollar, and then made a table as shown below. Study the table. Then do Numbers 7 and 8.

Electric Bills

Month	Amount
January	$59
February	$51
March	$48
April	$37
May	$48
June	$63
July	$72

7. What was her mean (average) monthly electric bill for the past 7 months?

a $48

b $51

c $54

d $63

8. What was her median monthly bill for the past 7 months?

a $37

b $48

c $51

d $54

9. Isabella conducted a survey to find out what internet provider was being used the most by those in her community of 50,000. She surveyed 50 people in her department at her workplace of 600 employees. For which of these groups will the information from this survey be most valid?

   a the entire county

   b the entire community

   c the employees at her workplace

   d the employees in her department

As a promotion for its product, a company offered various prizes. The prizes and the odds of winning each prize are shown in the table below. Study the table. Then do Number 10.

Prize	Odds
Pair of movie tickets	1:20
Camera	1:2,000
Television	1:10,000
Trip to New York City	1:1,000,000

10. Armando received a letter informing him he had won a prize. Based on the odds in the table, which prize did he most likely win?

    a pair of movie tickets

    b camera

    c television

    d trip to New York City

For Numbers 11 through 14, write your answers.

The table below shows the number of miles per gallon obtained by various cars, and the mean (average) miles per gallon for all the cars. Study the table. Then do Number 11.

Car	Miles per Gallon
Bluefin	23.7
Jetty	17.1
Roadhog	12.6
Speedster	?
Charger	26.7
Panther	18.2
Mean	22.1

11. Based on the information in the table, what is the number of miles per gallon obtained by the Speedster?

_____

12. The following prizes were offered at a raffle:

- 5 certificates for a local restaurant
- 10 certificates for a local music store
- 9 certificates for a book
- 15 pairs of movie passes
- 1 certificate for a grand trip for two

Tran bought 12 tickets out of a total of 400 that were sold for the raffle. What is the probability that Tran could win a pair of movie passes or a certificate for a local music store?

_____

The table below shows the test scores Lisa made on her first 5 tests. Study the table. Then do Numbers 13 and 14.

Lisa's Test Scores

Test	1	2	3	4	5	6
Score	93	89	76	92	94	?

13. To earn an A in her class, Lisa must have at least a mean (average) test score of 90. What is the minimum score she needs to make on her next test to earn an A?

_____

14. If there are 2 more tests to be taken, what is the mean (average) score she will need to score on both tests to receive an A?

_____

Reminder

To find the average (mean) of a set of numbers, find their sum and then divide the sum by the number of addends. For example, the average of 7, 13, 10, and 6 is as follows:

$$\frac{7 + 13 + 10 + 6}{4} = \frac{36}{4} = 9$$

NOTES

PATTERNS, FUNCTIONS, ALGEBRA

A *pattern* is the arrangement of numbers or elements in a particular order or sequence. The order or sequence depends on a specific rule, such as "add 3" or "multiply by 5."

A *function* is a set of ordered pairs (a relation) in which the value of the first number (the domain) is paired with exactly one value of the second number (the range).

Algebra is the process of using variables (letters or boxes) to represent unknown numbers. The value of the variables can be found by performing mathematical operations using the rules of algebra.

Patterns, Functions, Algebra includes subskills, such as Variable, Expression, Equation, Function, Inequality, and Linear Equations.

Look at this example of patterns, functions, algebra. Choose your answer for each problem.

EXAMPLE	ANSWER

What value of y makes this equation true?

$$5y + 8 = 10$$

a $\quad y = {}^-3$

b $\quad y = 10$

c $\quad y = \frac{2}{5}$

d $\quad y = \frac{18}{5}$

- **Answer *a* is not** correct. The number 8 was correctly subtracted from both sides of the equation to get $5y = 2$, but the next step, subtracting 5 from both sides, was incorrect.

- **Answer *b* is not** correct. The number 8 was correctly subtracted from both sides to get $5y = 2$, but the next steps, multiplying 2 by 5 and dividing 5y by 5, were incorrect.

- **Answer *c* is correct.** The first step was to subtract 8 from both sides to get $5y = 2$. Then both sides were divided by 5 to get the correct answer.

- **Answer *d* is not** correct. The number 8 was added to the right side instead of subtracted. Next, both sides were divided by 5, giving the incorrect equation $5y = 18$.

Do these patterns, functions, algebra problems. First, try Numbers 1 and 2 for practice.

1. What number is missing from the number pattern below?

   1, 1, 2, 4, 3, 9, 4, _____, 5, 25

   a 8

   b 12

   c 16

   d 20

   ANSWER c is correct. The pattern is 1, 1^2, 2, 2^2, 3, 3^2, 4, 4^2, 5, 5^2, etc. Since $4^2 = 16$, answer c is correct.

2. Which of these number lines shows the solution to the inequality $3x \geq {}^-12$?

   a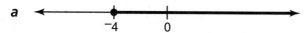

   b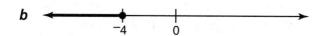

   c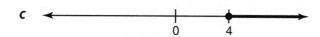

   d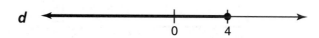

   ANSWER a is correct. To solve the inequality, divide both sides by 3. The result is $x \geq {}^-4$, which is graphed in choice a.

Now you are ready to do more problems. The answers to the problems in this section can be found in the back of this workbook.

3. In the table below, Input numbers (x) have been changed to Output numbers (y) by using a certain rule.

Input (x)	Output (y)
2	3
4	15
6	35
8	63

Which of these equations is the rule used to make this table?

a $y = x^2 + 1$

b $y = 3x + 3$

c $y = x^2 - 1$

d $y = 8x - 1$

4. In the chart below, the numbers in Column A are changed to different numbers in Column B by applying a common rule. If A > B for all numbers, which of these could be the rule?

a   Add 3.

b   Subtract 3.

c   Divide by 2.

d   Multiply by 2.

A	B
3	?
6	3
⁻8	?

When finding the rule used to make an Input-Output table, make sure the rule works for every row of the table.

5. Which of these symbols could go in the square box to make this number sentence true?

$$10^3 \ \square \ 3^{10}$$

a   =

b   <

c   >

d   None of these

6. What number should go in the square box to make this number sentence true?

$$5 + \frac{\square}{2} = 13$$

a   4

b   8

c   10

d   16

To solve an inequality, use the same steps as when solving an equation. But if you multiply or divide both sides of the inequality by a negative number, reverse the sign of the inequality. For example:

If $5y > 10$, then $y > 2$.
If $^-5y > 10$, then $y < ^-2$.

The chart below shows the rates charged by a rental car company. Study the chart. Then do Numbers 7 through 9.

Rental Car Rates

Type of Car	Rental Fee (per day)	Mileage Charge
Economy	$35	First 100 miles free, then $0.10 per mile
Mid-size	$45	First 200 miles free, then $0.15 per mile
Luxury	$60	First 300 miles free, then $0.20 per mile

7. Ronaldo rented a luxury car for 3 days and drove a total of 500 miles. Which of these number sentences should he use to find the total cost?

   a ☐ = 3 + $60 + $0.20(200)

   b ☐ = 3 + $60 + $0.20(500)

   c ☐ = 3 × $60 + $0.20(200)

   d ☐ = 3 × $60 + $0.20(500)

8. Which of these equations gives T, the total cost in dollars of renting an economy car for n days and driving a total of x miles? (Assume $x > 100$.)

    a $T = 35n + 0.1(x + 100)$

    b $T = 35n + 0.1(x - 100)$

    c $T = 35n + 10(x + 100)$

    d $T = 35n + 10(x - 100)$

9. Carolyn rented a mid-size car for 5 days. The total cost of the rental was $279. Which of these equations could be solved to find x, the number of miles Carolyn drove?

    a $5(45) + 0.15(x - 200) = 279$

    b $5(45) + 0.15(x + 200) = 279$

    c $5[45 + 0.15(x - 200)] = 279$

    d $5[45 + 0.15(x + 200)] = 279$

The product of two variables or a number and a variable may be written without the multiplication sign. For example, $a \times b$ can be written as ab, and $5 \times z$ can be written as $5z$.

Reminder

Preston earns $15 per hour at his regular job as a computer technician. He also earns $40 per hour teaching evening classes at the community college. Use this information to help you do Numbers 10 and 11.

10. Last week, Preston earned a total of $925. If he worked 10 hours teaching, how many hours did he work as a computer technician?

    a 13

    b 19

    c 35

    d 52

11. Which of these equations can be solved to find T, the total amount in dollars Preston earns in a month if he works x hours as a computer technician and y hours teaching?

    a $T = 55xy$

    b $T = 55(x + y)$

    c $T = 40x + 15y$

    d $T = 15x + 40y$

12. If $4x - 2 < 10$, then x could be

    a   3 only

    b   any number less than 3

    c   2 only

    d   any number greater than 2

The diagram below shows the tiles that have been used to cover the first 3 feet of a hallway that is 10 feet long. Study the diagram. Then do Number 13.

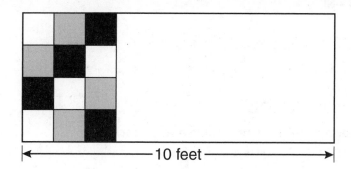

13. If the pattern continues, how many white tiles in all will be used to cover the hallway?

    a   13

    b   14

    c   15

    d   16

For Numbers 14 through 17, write your answers.

14. What number goes in both boxes to make this number sentence true?

$$2 \times \boxed{} = 72 \div \boxed{}$$

_____

15. What value of n makes this equation true?

$$\sqrt{2n} = 4$$

_____

Reminder

Finding the square root of a number is the inverse of squaring a number. So the square root of 25 (written $\sqrt{25}$) is 5, because $5^2 = 25$.

16. If Lawrence walked 12 miles in 6 hours at a steady pace, how far did he walk in 30 minutes?

_____

The *distance* traveled by a moving object is equal to its average *rate* of speed multiplied by the *time* it travels ($d = rt$).

17. How many whole numbers satisfy **both** of the inequalities below?

$$n \geq 2 \quad \text{AND} \quad n \leq 9$$

_____

The symbol "$<$" means "less than." Therefore, $5 < 6$ is true but $6 < 6$ is false. However, the symbol "$\leq$" means "less than or equal to," so $6 \leq 6$ is true. Similarly, "$>$" means "greater than" and "$\geq$" means "greater than or equal to."

PROBLEM SOLVING AND REASONING

Problem solving and reasoning utilizes the processes to formulate problems, to determine and apply strategies to solve problems, and to evaluate and justify solutions.

Problem Solving and Reasoning includes subskills, such as Solve Problem, Identify Missing/Extra Information, Model Problem Situation, Solution, and Evaluate Solution.

Look at these examples of problem solving and reasoning. Choose your answer for each problem.

EXAMPLE	ANSWER

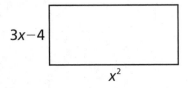

$3x - 4$

x^2

Which of these expressions gives the area of the rectangle above?

a $x^2 + 3x - 4$

b $2x^2 + 6x - 8$

c $3x^3 - 4$

d $3x^3 - 4x^2$

- **Answer a** is **not** correct. The length and width were added instead of multiplied.

- **Answer b** is **not** correct. This is the perimeter of the rectangle.

- **Answer c** is **not** correct. Both terms of $3x - 4$ must be multiplied by x^2.

- **Answer d** is correct. To find the area, the length and width must be multiplied. For this problem, use the distributive property: $x^2(3x - 4) = 3x^3 - 4x^2$.

Reminder

To solve problems, read the entire problem carefully. Plan a strategy to solve the problem, and then use the strategy. State the answer to the problem, and then check the answer to make sure it is reasonable.

| EXAMPLE | ANSWER |

Softball Jerseys

Size	Price
Medium	$5.00
Large	$6.50

Medium size softball jerseys cost $5.00 each, and large size jerseys cost $6.50 each. Joseph ordered 4 jerseys for the softball team. Which of these could **not** be the amount of money Joseph spent on the jerseys?

a $21.50

b $26.00

c $20.00

d $22.00

- **Answer a** is **not** correct.
  $21.50 = 3 \times \$5.00 + 1 \times \$6.50$

- **Answer b** is **not** correct.
  $26.00 = 4 \times \$6.50$

- **Answer c** is **not** correct.
  $20.00 = 4 \times \$5.00$

- **Answer d** is correct. There is no way to combine $5.00 and $6.50 to make $22.00.

**Do these problem solving and reasoning problems.
First, try Numbers 1 and 2 for practice.**

1. Roger is saving money for a new motorcycle that costs $15,500. He plans to save 15% of his monthly income to pay for the motorcycle. He already has $1,500 saved from the sale of his old motorcycle.

   What additional information is needed to determine the number of months Roger must save in order to have enough money to purchase the new motorcycle?

   a his monthly income amount

   b the amount of his monthly bills

   c the selling price of his old motorcycle

   d the buying price of his old motorcycle

   ANSWER *a* is correct. If Roger's monthly income is known, the monthly income can be multiplied by 15% to determine how much he saves per month. Then, the amount already saved ($1,500) should be subtracted from the buying price ($15,500) to determine the remaining balance for the cost of the new motorcycle. This difference can then be divided by the monthly amount saved in order to determine the number of months Roger will need to save.

2. A pool cleaner charges $35 to vacuum a pool, plus an additional $12 for each gallon ($g$) of a chlorine solution added to the water. Which of these equations could be used to determine the total amount of money (m) the pool cleaner charges to clean a pool?

   a $m = (\$12 + g) + \$35$

   b $m = \$12(\$35 + g)$

   c $m = \$35 + \$12g$

   d $m = \$35(\$12) + g$

ANSWER c is correct. The total amount of gallons used (g) should be multiplied by the cost ($12) for each gallon. This product should then be added to $35 in order to find the total cost of cleaning one pool.

Now you are ready to do more problems. The answers to the problems in this section can be found in the back of this workbook.

3. The Alvarez family has a large van with a gasoline tank capacity of 18 gallons. The van gets an average of 16 miles per gallon of gasoline. If the van is driven for 36 miles, what percent of the gasoline tank capacity is used?

   a 2.25%

   b 6.25%

   c 12.5%

   d 15.75%

4. A carpenter cuts a board into two pieces, as shown below.

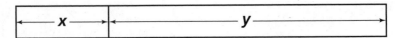

   The longer piece (*y*) is one foot greater than twice the length of the shorter piece (*x*). Which of these equations correctly represents this relationship?

   a 2*x* = *y* + 1

   b 2*y* = *x* − 1

   c 2*y* = *x* + 1

   d 2*x* = *y* − 1

5. David is training for a marathon for a period of 8 weeks. He recorded the total weekly number of miles he ran for the first 6 weeks, as shown on the chart below.

Training Chart

Week	Total Miles
1	36
2	45
3	24
4	45
5	52
6	38
7	?
8	?

How many more **total** miles must he run in weeks 7 and 8 in order to average 60 miles a week for the entire 8 weeks of training?

a 60 miles

b 120 miles

c 240 miles

d 480 miles

The chart below shows the inventory, cost, and profit data for a retail clothing store. Study the chart. Then do Number 6.

Inventory Ledger

Item Description	Wholesale Cost	Units Sold	Selling Price	Total Profit
Men's Shirt	$15.00	58	$30.00	$870.00
Women's Blouse	$20.00	44	$44.00	$1, 056.00
Men's Jeans	$25.00	88	$52.00	$2,200.00
Women's Trousers	$22.00	42	$40.00	$756.00
			Grand Total	$4,882.00

6. To calculate the Total Profit, the store bookkeeper subtracts the Wholesale Cost from the Selling Price, and then multiplies the difference by the number of Units Sold. For which item did the bookkeeper make an error when calculating the Total Profit?

   a   Men's Shirts

   b   Women's Blouses

   c   Men's Jeans

   d   Women's Trousers

7. The diagram below shows how one-square-foot tiles are being laid as a border around a rectangular pool.

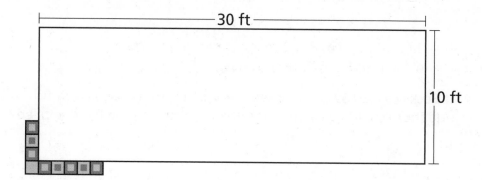

Which of these expressions could be used to find the total number of tiles needed to completely border the pool?

a $(2 \times 31) + (2 \times 11)$

b $10 \times 30 + 4$

c $(2 \times 32) + (2 \times 12)$

d 12×32

8. Jerry works 6 hours a day as a typist, and is paid for the number of pages he types each day. Each page has a capacity of 500 words, and Jerry types an average of 50 words per minute. What information is missing and needed to determine the amount of money Jerry makes per day as a typist?

a the number of words that fill a page

b the number of hours he works per day

c the amount of money paid for each typed page

d the average number of words per minute that he types

9. Becky invests $150 of her monthly salary into a savings account at a local bank. The bank uses the following formula to calculate the amount of interest she earns.

i = **P**r**t**
(*i* = interest earned, *P* = principal amount invested,
r = interest rate, *t* = time in years)

If Becky earned $24.75 in interest for 6 months of savings, which of these equations could be used to find the interest rate the bank applied?

a $r = \dfrac{\$24.75}{\$900 \times 0.5}$

b $r = \dfrac{\$24.75}{\$150 \times 6}$

c $r = \dfrac{\$900 \times 0.5}{\$24.75}$

d $r = \dfrac{\$24.75}{150}$

10. The table below shows the number of weeks Josh trained for several one-mile races, and his running time for the races.

Josh's Training and Mile Times

Mile Race	Weeks of Training	Time (minutes/seconds)
A	40	7:30
B	45	?
C	55	6:00
D	60	5:30

After Race A, Josh increased the number of weeks of training. He discovered that for every additional ten weeks of training, his one-mile running time decreased by 60 seconds. If this decrease is constant, what should be Josh's running time for Race B?

a 6:30

b 6:45

c 7:00

d 7:15

For Numbers 11 through 14, write your answers.

11. A dry cleaner charges $5.00 to clean one pair of pants, $3.50 to clean a shirt, and $12.00 to clean a dress coat. The dry cleaner charged $44.25 to clean 1 dress coat, 5 shirts, and 3 pairs of pants. Was this charge correct? Show why or why not on the line below.

_____

12. The area of a rectangular soccer field is 7,500 square feet. The length of the field is 150 feet. What is the perimeter of the soccer field?

_____

13. An agriculture center has a large cylindrical water storage tank. The tank is 40 feet in height and has a volume of 50,240 cubic feet. What is the diameter of the tank?

$V = \pi r^2 h$

(Use 3.14 for π.)

_____

Reminder

To find the area of a rectangle, use the formula $A = lw$.
To find the perimeter of a rectangle, use the formula $P = 2l + 2w$.

14. An architect wants to measure the height of a building by comparing it with the height of a nearby flagpole. He made a drawing, as shown below.

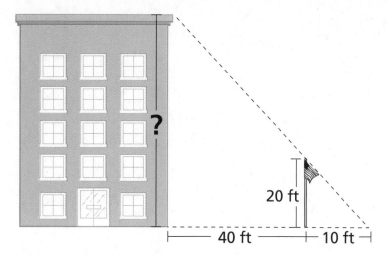

Note: The figure is not drawn to scale.

What is the height of the building?

_____

The corresponding sides of similar triangles are proportional. If △ABC is similar to △XYZ, then one of the proportions is as follows:

$$\frac{\overline{AB}}{\overline{AC}} = \frac{\overline{XY}}{\overline{XZ}}$$

Reminder

Question	Answer	MATH COMPUTATION: Decimals, Level A
3	*a*	$43.84 + 29.672 = 73.512$
4	*e*	Line up the decimal points and solve: $534.32 + 42.2 = 576.52$. Since this answer is not given, the correct answer is choice *e*.
5	*b*	The difference between the decimals is 7.01.
6	*b*	The difference between the decimals is 0.026.
7	*a*	The product is 0.56. There is one decimal place in each factor, so the product must have two decimal places.
8	*b*	There are two zeros in 100, so move the decimal point two places to the right to get 52.7.
9	*b*	Convert $82.46 \div 0.14$ to $8{,}246 \div 14$ by multiplying both numbers by 100, and then divide: $8{,}246 \div 14 = 589$.
10	*e*	Convert $45 \div 0.01$ to $4{,}500 \div 1$ by multiplying both numbers by 100, and then divide to get 4,500. Since this answer is not given, the correct answer is choice *e*.
11		**42.1962** Line up the decimal points and add to get 42.1962.
12		**5.987** Line up the decimal points and subtract to get 5.987.
13		**1.0920** There are two decimal places in each factor, so the product must have 4 decimal places.
14		**0.225** Convert $0.27 \div 1.2$ to $2.7 \div 12$ by multiplying both numbers by 10. Then divide to get 0.225.

Question	Answer	MATH COMPUTATION: Fractions, Level A
3	*e*	$\frac{2}{4} + \frac{4}{4} = \frac{6}{4} = \frac{3}{2} = 1\frac{1}{2}$ Since this answer is not given, the correct answer is choice *e*.
4	*d*	$1\frac{2}{3} + 3\frac{3}{4} = 1\frac{8}{12} + 3\frac{9}{12} = 4\frac{17}{12} = 5\frac{5}{12}$
5	*c*	$\frac{9}{16} - \frac{3}{16} = \frac{6}{16} = \frac{3}{8}$
6	*d*	$\frac{3}{4} - \frac{1}{5} = \frac{15}{20} - \frac{4}{20} = \frac{11}{20}$
7	*e*	$\frac{2}{3} \times \frac{3}{10} = \frac{6}{30} = \frac{1}{5}$ Since this answer is not given, the correct answer is choice *e*.
8	*b*	$\frac{5}{4} \times \frac{10}{3} = \frac{50}{12} = \frac{25}{6}$
9	*d*	$\frac{4}{5} \div \frac{1}{5} = \frac{4}{5} \times \frac{5}{1} = \frac{20}{5} = 4$
10	*a*	$2\frac{1}{2} \times \frac{4}{5} = \frac{5}{2} \times \frac{4}{5} = \frac{20}{10} = 2$
11		$\mathbf{4\frac{19}{40}}$ $1\frac{7}{8} + 2\frac{3}{5} = 1\frac{35}{40} + 2\frac{24}{40} = 3\frac{59}{40} = 4\frac{19}{40}$
12		$\mathbf{2\frac{5}{16}}$ $4\frac{5}{8} - 2\frac{5}{16} = 4\frac{10}{16} - 2\frac{5}{16} = 2\frac{5}{16}$
13		$\mathbf{\frac{11}{4}}$ or $\mathbf{2\frac{3}{4}}$ $\frac{11}{24} \times 6 = \frac{66}{24} = \frac{11}{4}$
14		$\mathbf{\frac{8}{3}}$ or $\mathbf{2\frac{2}{3}}$ $\frac{14}{9} \div \frac{7}{12} = \frac{14}{9} \times \frac{12}{7} = \frac{2}{3} \times \frac{4}{1}$ (after reducing) $= \frac{8}{3}$

Answer Key

Question	Answer	MATH COMPUTATION: Integers, Level A
3	*d*	To add with unlike signs, subtract the smaller absolute value from the larger absolute value, and keep the original sign of the number with the larger absolute value: To add $^-3 + 2$: $\|^-3\| - \|2\| = 3 - 2 = 1$. Since the original sign of the number with the larger absolute value (3) is negative, the result (1) must be negative. $^-3 + 2 = ^-1$
4	*c*	$\| 14 \| - \| ^-7\| = 14 - 7 = 7$ Since 14 is the greater absolute value, the result is positive. $14 + (^-7) = 7$
5	*c*	Following the subtraction rule: $16 - (^-13) = 16 + (13) = 29$.
6	*a*	The product of two integers with unlike signs is always negative. $8 \times ^-11 = ^-88$
7	*a*	Following the subtraction rule: $^-4 - (^-10) = ^-4 + (10)$. Following the addition rule with unlike signs: $\| 10 \| - \| ^-4 \| = 10 - 4 = 6$.
8	*c*	The product of two integers with like signs is always positive. $^-16 \times (^-16) = 256$
9	*d*	The quotient of two integers with like signs is always positive. $^-24 \div ^-3 = 8$
10	*a*	The quotient of two integers with unlike signs is always negative. $^-40 \div 5 = ^-8$
11		**$^-50$** To add integers with like signs, add and keep the sign. $^-40 + (^-10) = ^-50$
12		**400** $\| 200 ^- 600\| = \| ^-400 \| = 400$
13		**$^-120$** The product of an odd number of negative integers is always negative. $^-4 \times ^-5 = 20$; $20 \times ^-6 = ^-120$
14		**1** The quotient of two integers with like signs is always positive. $^-45 \div (^-45) = 1$
		MATH COMPUTATION: Percents, Level A
3	*e*	Convert 6% to 0.06 and multiply. $0.06 \times \$3 = \$0.18$ Since the answer is not given, the correct answer is choice *e*.
4	*d*	Convert 4.8% to 0.048 and multiply. $0.048 \times 80 = 3.84$
5	*d*	$60 \div 75 = 0.8 = 80\%$
6	*c*	$45 \div 36 = 1.25 = 125\%$
7	*c*	Convert 90% to 0.9 and divide. $12.6 \div 0.9 = 126 \div 9 = 14$
8	*a*	Convert 150% to 1.5 and divide. $900 \div 1.5 = 9{,}000 \div 15 = 600$
9	*c*	Convert $1\frac{1}{2}$% to 0.015 and divide. $\$6 \div 0.015 = 6{,}000 \div 15 = \$400$
10		**0.08** Convert 0.4% to 0.004 and multiply. $0.004 \times 20 = 0.08$
11		**5%** $0.25 \div 5 = 0.05 = 5\%$
12		**$22** Convert 8% to 0.08 and divide. $\$1.76 \div 0.08 = 176 \div 8 = \$22$
13		**1,600** Convert 0.5% to 0.005 and divide. $8 \div 0.005 = 8{,}000 \div 5 = 1{,}600$

Answer Key

Question	Answer	MATH COMPUTATION: Order of Operations, Level A
3	*d*	$(26 \div 2 - 3)^2 = (13 - 3)^2 = (10)^2 = 100$
4	*c*	$8 + 4(3) \div 6 - 2 = 8 + 12 \div 6 - 2 = 8 + 2 - 2 = 8$
5	*a*	$8^2 - 8^2 \div 4(2) = 64 - 64 \div 4(2) = 64 - 16(2) = 64 - 32 = 32$
6	*b*	$3 \times 8 - 4 \div 2 = 24 - 2 = 22$
7	*a*	$40 \div 2^3 + 2 \times 4 - 1 = 40 \div 8 + 8 - 1 = 5 + 8 - 1 = 12$
8	*a*	$(18 \div 9 - 9) \times 3 - 2^2 = (2 - 9) \times 3 - 4 = {}^-7 \times 3 - 4 = {}^-21 - 4 = {}^-25$
9	*c*	$32 \div 4 \times 2 + 4 \div 2 = 8 \times 2 + 2 = 16 + 2 = 18$
10	*a*	$14 - ({}^-7) + 14 \div 7 = 14 - ({}^-7) + 2 = 21 + 2 = 23$
11		**8** $\ {}^-108 \div ({}^-2) \div 6 - 1 = 54 \div 6 - 1 = 9 - 1 = 8$
12		**16** $\ 56 \div 7 - 4 \times {}^-2 = 8 + 8 = 16$
13		**6** $\ 2^2 \div 4 + 13 - 4 \times 2 = 4 \div 4 + 13 - 8 = 1 + 13 - 8 = 6$
14		**22** $\ 36 \div 6 + 88 \div 11 \times 2 = 6 + 8 \times 2 = 6 + 16 = 22$
		MATH COMPUTATION: Algebraic Operations, Level A
3	*c*	$8^{15} \div 8^3 = 8^{15-3} = 8^{12}$
4	*e*	$(10^2)^6 = 10^{2 \times 6} = 10^{12}$ Since the answer is not given, the correct answer is choice *e*.
5	*a*	$5x + 3x = (5 + 3)\,x = 8x$
6	*c*	$8y - y = (8 - 1)y = 7y$
7	*d*	Use the distributive property: $4(2b + 5) = 4(2b) + 4(5) = 8b + 20$.
8	*d*	$2x + 3x(4 - y) = 2x + 3x(4) - 3x(y) = 2x + 12x - 3xy = 14x - 3xy$
9	*d*	$\frac{(6y^2 + 14y)}{2y} = \frac{6y^2}{2y} + \frac{14y}{2y} = 3y + 7$
10	*d*	$(3a - 5)^2 = (3a - 5)(3a - 5) = (3a)(3a) + 3a({}^-5) - 5(3a) - 5({}^-5) = 9a^2 - 15a - 15a + 25 = 9a^2 - 30a + 25$
11		**5^8** $\ (5^2)^4 = 5^{2 \times 4} = 5^8$
12		**$9z + 18$** $\ 12z - 3(z - 6) = 12z - 3(z) - 3({}^-6) = 12z - 3z + 18 = 9z + 18$
13		**$x^2 - 10x + 16$** $\ (x - 2)(x - 8) = x^2 - 8x - 2x + 16 = x^2 - 10x + 16$
14		**$5a - 4$** $\ \frac{(15a^2 = 12a)}{3a} = \frac{15a^2}{3a} - \frac{12a}{3a} = 5a - 4$

Answer Key

Question	Answer	APPLIED MATHEMATICS: Number and Number Operations, Level A
3	d	The pattern is to add 0.7 to each preceding number. $3.5 + 0.7 = 4.2$
4	a	Divide 22 by 7: $22 \div 7 = 3$ R 1. Then write the remainder as a fraction to obtain $3\frac{1}{7}$.
5	b	The final digit (4) in the number 3.14 is located in the hundredth place value, so the last stated word must be "hundredths." Therefore, 3.14 is written "three and fourteen hundredths."
6	c	Overall, there were 31% in favor of Proposition 1. Therefore, 31% of 1,000 = $0.31 \times 1,000 = 310$.
7	b	Find the difference between the two propositions. $86\% - 56\% = 30\%$. Then take 30% of 250. $30\% \times 250 = 0.3 \times 250 = 75$
8	b	For Proposition 2, the percent in favor by each age group decreased by 8%.
9	a	$30\% = \frac{30}{100} = \frac{3}{10}$
10	d	To convert 48% to a decimal, move the decimal point two places to the left and drop the percent sign. $48\% = 0.48$
11	c	To find 1% of 1 million, multiply 0.01 by 1,000,000.
12	a	The total cost must equal $14.95 + 0.06 \times $14.95. Using the distributive property, the $14.95 can be factored out and the expression can be rewritten as $14.95(1 + 0.06) = $14.95(1.06), or 1.06($14.95), using the commutative property.
13	a	68 vehicles per minute is equivalent to 68 vehicles per 60 seconds. Since a correct proportion must maintain a proper order, $\frac{L \text{ vehicles}}{1 \text{ second}} = \frac{68 \text{ vehicles}}{60 \text{ seconds}}$ is the only correct proportion.
14	c	Subtract to find the increase in traffic level. Then divide by the amount of traffic in 1980 to find the percent increase in traffic. $30 - 20 = 10$; $10 \div 20 = 0.5 = 50\%$
15	a	Since $10^{-5} = 0.00001$, then $4.673 \times 0.00001 = 0.00004673$.
16	d	A number written in scientific notation must contain a number between 1 and 10, multiplied by a power of ten. To make 186,000 become a number between 1 and 10, the decimal point must be moved five places to the left. To do this, the number is multiplied by $\frac{10^5}{10^5}$ (which is the number 1 written in a different form). $186,000 \times \frac{10^5}{10^5} = \frac{186,000}{10^5} \times 10^5 = 1.86 \times 10^5$
17	c	To convert a decimal to a percent, move the decimal point two places to the right and attach a percent symbol.
18	b	Since $\sqrt{N} = x$, squaring both sides will result in $N = x^2$
19		**25%** One out of four videos is free, so $\frac{1}{4} = 0.25 = 25\%$, which is the percent discount.
20		**3** For each group of four videotapes, one is free. Divide by 4 to find the number of groups. $12 \div 4 = 3$

Question	Answer	APPLIED MATHEMATICS: Number and Number Operations, Level A (cont)
21		**70** The ratio of skilled to unskilled laborers is 3:7, which means that 7 out of 10 laborers are unskilled. Use a proportion to find the number of unskilled laborers out of 100 laborers. $\frac{7}{10} = \frac{x}{100}$; $10x = 700$; $\frac{10x}{10} = \frac{700}{10}$; $x = 70$.
22		**0.875** $7 \div 8 = 7.000 \div 8 = 0.875$
23		**2** The cube root of a number is one of the three equal factors of that number. Since $2 \times 2 \times 2 = 8$, 2 is the cube root of 8.
24		**4×10^{-3}** To write 0.004 in scientific notation, the decimal point must be moved three places to the right. To do this, the number is multiplied by $\frac{10^3}{10^3}$ (which is the number 1 written in a different form). $0.004 \times \frac{10^3}{10^3} = (0.004 \times 10^3) \times \frac{1}{10^3} = 4 \times \frac{1}{10^3} = 4 \times 10^{-3}$

Question	Answer	APPLIED MATHEMATICS: Computation in Context, Level A
3	*a*	$8{,}300 \div 2{,}000 = 4.15$ tons
4	*d*	The percent decrease is equal to the decrease amount divided by the original amount. $5.0 - 4.5 = 0.5$ (decrease amount); $0.5 \div 5 = 0.1 = 10\%$
5	*d*	Let x = the box length, and $\frac{1}{3}x$ = the cab length. Since the box and cab together make the total length, $x + \frac{1}{3}x = 48$; $\frac{4}{3}x = 48$; $x = 48(\frac{3}{4})$; $x = 36$ feet.
6	*c*	$4.5 \times 150 = 675$ miles
7	*c*	The selling price is the store cost (100%) added to the markup (20%). Therefore, 120% of \$20 = $1.2 \times \$20 = \$24$.
8	*b*	30% of \$50 = $0.3 \times \$50 = \$15$ This is the markup for one pair of slacks. $\$15 \times 100 = \$1{,}500$
9	*c*	5 shirts: $5 \times \$20 = \$100$; 6 ties: $6 \times \$12.50 = \$75$; $\$100 + \$75 = \$175$
10	*a*	Money saved on suit: $\$2.75 \times 20\% = \$275 \times 0.20 = \$55$. Money saved on tie: $\$12.5 \times 10\% = \$12.5 \times 0.10 = \$1.25$. Total saved: $\$55 + \$1.25 = \$56.25$
11		**\$74.80** If the discount is 15%, then the sale price must be 85% of the regular price. $0.85 \times \$88 = \$74.80$
12		**\$13.50** $\$9 \times 1.5 = \$13.50$
13		**\$1.80** $0.075 \times \$24 = \$1.80$
14		**\$560** $35 \times \$16 = 560$
15		**30 hours** Let x represent the number of hours Tim works, and $(50 - x)$ represent the number of hours Melinda works. Then $16x$ represents the amount Tim earns, and $24(50 - x)$ represents the amount Melinda earns. They each earn the same amount. $16x = 24(50 - x)$; $16x = 1{,}200 - 24x$; $40x = 1{,}200$; $x = 30$ hours

Answer Key

Question	Answer	APPLIED MATHEMATICS: Estimation, Level A
3	c	966,079 can round to 1,000,000, and 5,574,396 can round to 6,000,000. Then $\frac{1,000,000}{6,000,000} = \frac{1}{6} \approx$ 0.167 ≈ 16.7%, which lies between 15% and 20%.
4	a	Round both quantities to the nearest million and set up a ratio. 4,000,000 ÷ 6,000,000 = $\frac{4}{6} = \frac{2}{3}$
5	d	The digit to the right of the hundred place value is 8, so round up to get 387,500.
6	a	The digit to the right of the ten thousand place value is 4, so round down to get 5,570,000.
7	b	Fixed costs represent 11% of the budget, which can round to 10%. Therefore, 10% = $\frac{10}{100} = \frac{1}{10}$.
8	b	69% can round to 70% and $331,500 can round to $330,000. Then 70% of $330,000 = 0.7 × $330,000 = $231,000 which is nearest to $230,000. Or, $331,500 can round to $300,000. Then 70% of $300,000 = 0.7 × $300,000 = $210,000, which is nearest to $230,000.
9	b	1.52 can round to 1.5 and 4.87 can round to 5. Therefore, 1.5 ÷ 5 = 0.3. Or, 1.52 can round to 2. Then 2 ÷ 5 = 0.4, which is nearest to 0.3.
10	c	Vanessa buys groceries about 6 times every 4 months, or about 18 times a year. Round 18 up to 20, and $73 down to $70, and then multiply. (20 × $70 = $1,400) The amount is between $1,000 and $1,500.
11	d	It is obvious that more than $\frac{3}{4}$, or 75%, of the rectangle is shaded, so it seems that 88% is the best estimate.
12	b	Each of the sides $\overline{PO}$ and $\overline{MN}$ appears to be about 1.5 times the length of $\overline{AB}$. Therefore, 1.5 × 10 = 15 units for each side. Each of the sides $\overline{PM}$ and $\overline{ON}$ appears to be about one-half the length of $\overline{AB}$. Therefore, 0.5 × 10 = 5 units for each side. The estimated distance around is: 15 + 15 + 5 + 5 = 40 units.
13		**16.6430** The digit to the right of the thousandth place value is 9, so round up to get 16.6430.
14		**0.04** The number 0.84167 rounded to the nearest hundredth is 0.84, and rounded to the nearest tenth is 0.8. The difference between the answers is 0.84 − 0.8 = 0.04
15		**$9 or $10** 28 can be rounded to 30 and then multiplied: 30 × $0.15 = $4.50. Total fees: $5 + $4.50 = $9.50, which rounded to the nearest dollar is $10.
16		**$11 or $12** The first 20 checks are free, so 47 − 20 = 27 checks that will be charged. The 27 can be rounded to 30 and then multiplied: 30 × $0.15 = $4.50. Total fees: $7.50 + $4.50 = $12.

Question	Answer	APPLIED MATHEMATICS: Measurement, Level A
3	*b*	The difference between each of the three corresponding dimensions is 12" ($72 - 60 = 12$ or $36 - 24 = 12$ or $30 - 18 = 12$). Since this difference must represent the total thickness of any two opposite walls, the thickness of one wall is 6 inches ($12 \div 2 = 6$).
4	*a*	Convert the inches to feet: $60" \div 12 = 5$ ft.; $24" \div 12 = 2$ ft., and $18" \div 12 = 1.5$ ft. Use the formula: $V = lwh$; $5 \times 2 \times 1.5 = 15$ cubic feet
5	*a*	Use the formula: $d = rt$: $18 = 8t$; Solve for t and use the reflexive property: $t = \frac{18}{8}$; $t = \frac{9}{4} = 2\frac{1}{4}$ hours; It took her 2 hours 15 minutes to finish the race. She started at 9:00 A.M. Therefore, 9:00 A.M.+ 2 hours 15 minutes is 11:15 A.M.
6	*a*	When Sam landed in Los Angeles it was 7:52 P.M. in Boston ($2:40 + 5:12 = 7:52$). Since there is a 3-hour time difference between Eastern Standard Time and Pacific Standard Time, it was 4:52 P.M. in Los Angeles: 7:52 A.M. $- 3 = 4:52$ A.M.
7	*a*	The temperature increases 5° every 2 hours. There are two sets of 2-hour periods from 7 A.M. to 11 A.M. At 9 A.M., the temperature was ($0° + 5° = 5°$), or 5°C. At 11 A.M., the temperature was ($5° + 5° = 10°$) or 10°C.
8	*a*	The length of one inside edge is ($20 - 2$), or 18 meters. The total length of all the inside edges is (4×18), or 72 meters.
9	*c*	It took Sara $1\frac{1}{3}$ hours (20 minutes $= \frac{20}{60} = \frac{1}{3}$ hour) to finish 5 meters. Use and solve the proportion: $\frac{\frac{4}{3} \text{ hours}}{5 \text{ meters}} = \frac{x \text{ hours}}{20 \text{ meters}}$; $5x = \frac{80}{3}$; $x = \frac{80}{3} \times \frac{1}{5}$; $x = \frac{16}{3} = 5\frac{1}{3}$ hours, or 5 hours 20 minutes. 8:00 A.M. + 5 hours 20 minutes is 1:20 P.M.
10	*d*	Area of the deck: $20 \times 20 = 400$ square meters. Area of the pool: $\pi r^2 = 3.14 \times 4 \times 4 \approx 50$ square meters. Then $400 - 50 = 350$ square meters.
11	*c*	Sara earns ($\$8 \times 8$), or $64 for the first 8 hours, and ($\$12 \times 2$), or $24 for the additional 2 hours. $64 + $24 = $88
12	*d*	$V = lwh$; $V = 10 \times 3 \times 4 = 120$ cubic feet
13		**500 meters** 10 km $-$ 9.5 km $=$ 0.5 km. Since there are 1,000 meters in one kilometer, 0.5 km $\times$ 1,000 m $=$ 500 meters.
14		**1,000 cubic feet** Use the formula $V = e^3$ to find the volume: $V = 10 \times 10 \times 10 = 1,000$ cubic feet
15		**200 square feet** Half the perimeter of a rectangle is equal to a length plus a width. Therefore, $l + 10 = 30$; $l = 20$ feet. Use the formula $A = lw$ to find the area: $A = 20 \times 10 = 200$ square feet
16		**70 square inches** Use the formula $A = \frac{1}{2} bh$ to find the area: $A = \frac{1}{2} \times 14 \times 10 = 70$ square inches

Answer Key

Question	Answer	APPLIED MATHEMATICS: Geometry and Spatial Sense, Level A
3	d	A line contains an infinite number of points.
4	d	Segment $\overline{AE}$ Intersects plane EFGH, forming a 90° angle. Therefore, $\overline{AE}$ is perpendicular to plane EFGH.
5	b	The figure ACDE has four sides, and therefore is a quadrilateral.
6	a	A circle is the set of points equidistant from a given point called the center. In the diagram, the center of the circle is the origin and all the points on the circle are 5 units from the origin.
7	b	For a point to lie inside the circle, the coordinates of the point must be less than 5 and greater than ⁻5. Point (3,3) satisfies this condition and is located in the first quadrant inside the circle.
8	d	The endpoints of the diameter are ⁻5 and 5. The distance between these endpoints is 10 units: $5 - {}^{-}5 = 5 + 5 = 10$
9	c	There are 360° in a circle and all 10 angles have the same measure. $360 \div 10 = 36°$
10	b	In any triangle, the sum of the three angles must be 180°. A triangle cannot have two right angles because two right angles add up to 180°, leaving no degrees possible for a third angle.
11	d	The side view of a cylinder is a rectangle.
12	a	If figures are similar, their corresponding sides must be proportional. The dimensions 2 by 8 feet are proportional to 4 by 16 feet: $\frac{2}{8} = \frac{4}{16}$.
13	c	The point that represents the fire is located 6 units on the horizontal axis and 5.5 units on the vertical axis. Since the coordinate for the horizontal axis is always listed first, the coordinates for the fire are (6,5.5).
14	c	Looking from the Base Camp, the Lookout Tower must be to the right of the fire and Mt. Lucy must be to the left of the fire. Also, Mt. Lucy must be farther from the fire than the Lookout Tower. Choice **c** is the only diagram that satisfies these conditions.
15	d	Use the Pythagorean theorem ($a^2 + b^2 = c^2$) to represent the length of the hypotenuse of the right triangle formed by the Lookout Tower point, the fire point and Point (6,1): $(6-3)^2 + (5.5 - 1)^2 = 3^2 + 4.5^2 = c^2$; $\sqrt{3^2 + 4.5^2} = c$
16		**line segment** or **segment** or **hypotenuse** $\overline{CD}$ is a line segment. It contains points connected by a straight line between two endpoints. $\overline{CD}$ is also the hypotenuse of the right triangle. The hypotenuse is the longest side of any right triangle.
17		**10 feet** Since △ABE and △CBD are similar, a proportion can be used: $\frac{6}{x} = \frac{9}{15}$; $9x = 90$; $x = 10$.
18		**12 feet** Use the Pythagorean theorem: $9^2 + \overline{BD}^2 = 15^2$; $81 + \overline{BD}^2 = 225$; $\overline{BD}^2 = 144$; $\overline{BD} = 12$
19		**53°** The sum of the interior angles of a triangle is 180°, and the measure of a right angle is 90°. Therefore, $90° + 37° + x = 180°$; $127 + x = 180°$; $x = 53°$.

Answer Key

Question	Answer	APPLIED MATHEMATICS: Data Analysis, Level A
3	*b*	The labor section is about one-third of the circle graph. $\frac{1}{3} \times \$6,000,000 = \$2,000,000$
4	*a*	The planning section is about one-third the size of the materials section. The materials expense should then be about three times the planning expense.
5	*b*	The materials and labor sections make up about two-thirds of the circle graph. Then $\frac{2}{3} \approx 0.67 \approx 67\%$, which is nearest to 70%.
6	*c*	Since the area painted did not increase at all between 12 P.M. and 1 P.M., no one was painting during that time.
7	*a*	The line of the graph rises more steeply during the first four hours.
8	*d*	Since the rates differ depending on which night of the week one stays, this information is necessary.
9	*a*	The cost of the stays are as follows: 1) $130; 2) $130; 3) $120. Therefore, 1 and 2 cost the same.
10	*b*	Add the cost of the first minute and the four additional minutes: $0.75 + 4($0.15) = $0.75 + $0.60 = $1.35 per call. Multiply this amount by ten phone calls: $1.35 × 10 = $13.50. Then add the monthly fee: $13.50 + $3.50 = $17.00
11	*c*	Since Terrance makes several calls every day, he should choose the company that offers the lowest price for a five-minute call. Company 3 charges $1.05 for a five-minute call, while the other companies charge $1.35, $1.55, or $1.68.
12	*c*	The cost of the first 8 minutes is: 8 × $1.20 = $9.60. The cost of the additional x minutes is: $19.44 − $9.60 = $9.84. Then $0.12x = 9.84; x = 82$ minutes. Add the first minute for each of the 8 calls to the additional minutes: 8 + 82 = 90 minutes
13		**$9** 3 × $8.99 − 3 × $5.99 = $26.97 − $17.97 = $9; Or, $8.99 − $5.99 = $3 savings per day. For 3 days per week: 3 × $3 = $9
14		**$4.98** 2($8.99) − 2(10)($0.65) = $17.98 − $13 = $4.98
15		**$29.87** 2 × $8.99 + $7.99 + 6 × $0.65 = $17.98 + $7.99 + $3.90 = $29.87
16		**Two** The temperature variation was the same whenever the two lines intersected.
		APPLIED MATHEMATICS: Statistics and Probability, Level A
3	*c*	The spinner is most likely to stop on the color that contains the greatest area in the circle. Four of the twelve sections are green, which is more than any other color. Therefore, the spinner is most likely to stop on green.
4	*b*	The spinner will have an equal chance on stopping on the colors that contain the same area in the circle. Blue and red both contain the same areas since they are both in 2 equal sections.
5	*b*	The surveys in choices A and D are bias, since only persons who use the library are sampled. The survey in choice C is bias, since only persons entering the city hall are sampled.

Answer Key

Question	Answer	APPLIED MATHEMATICS: Statistics and Probability, Level A (cont.)
6	c	Out of a total of 90 drinks, 24 are cola drinks. Therefore, the probability of selecting a cola is 24 out of 90, or $\frac{24}{90}$ or $\frac{4}{15}$
7	c	($59 + $51 + $48 + $37 + $48 + $63 + $72) ÷ 7 = $378 ÷ 7 = $54
8	c	The median is the middle value after the numbers have been placed in ascending order. The ascending order is: [$37, $48, $48, $51, $59, $63, $72] The middle value is $51.
9	d	Since Isabella only surveyed people in her department, the information she receives would be most valid to the employees in her department.
10	a	The best chance for winning a prize is 1 out of 20. Therefore, Armando most likely won a pair of movie tickets.
11		**34.3 miles per gallon** [23.7 + 17.1 + 12.6 + 26.7 + 18.2 = 98.3]; 6 × 22.1 = 132.6; Therefore 132.6 − 98.3 = 34.3
12		$\frac{3}{160}$ The probability of Tran's tickets being drawn is 12 out of 400, or $\frac{12}{400}$ or $\frac{3}{100}$. The probability of winning a certificate for movie passes or for a music store is 25 out of 40 prizes, or $\frac{25}{40}$ or $\frac{5}{8}$. The probability of both occurring is $\frac{3}{100} \times \frac{5}{8} = \frac{3}{160}$.
13		**96** To obtain an average of 90 on 6 tests, Lisa must score a total of (90 × 6), or 540 points. She presently has a total of (93 + 89 + 76 + 92 + 94), or 444 points. She must then earn a score of at least (540 − 444), or 96 points, to earn an A.
14		**93** To obtain an average of 90 points after 7 tests, Lisa must score a total of (90 × 7), or 630 points. She presently has a total of (93 + 89 + 76 + 92 + 94), or 444 points. She must score a total of (630 − 444), or 186 points on the next two tests. The mean (average) of these two test scores is $\frac{186}{2}$, or 93. OR Since a score of 96 will give her a 90 average on the 6th test, she will then need to score a 90 on the 7th test to maintain the A average. The mean (average) of the 6th and 7th test scores is $(\frac{96 + 90}{2})$, or $\frac{186}{2}$, or 93.
		APPLIED MATHEMATICS: Patterns, Functions, Algebra, Level A
3	c	The Output is always one less than the square of the Input, which is given by the equation $y = x^2 - 1$.
4	b	Using the given numbers in the table (if A = 6, then B = 3), the only possibilities are choices **b** and **c**. Dividing by 2 does not hold true when A is a negative number. Subtraction is the only operation that will *always* make B less than A.
5	b	10^3 = 10 × 10 × 10 = 1.000 and 3^{10} = 3 × 3 × 3 × 3 × 3 × 3 × 3 × 3 × 3 × 3 = 59,049; 1.000 < 59,049
6	d	$5 + \frac{x}{2} = 13$; $2(5 + \frac{x}{2}) = 2(13)$; 10 + x = 26; x = 16
7	c	Total cost is: 3 × $60 + $0.20(500 − 300) = 3 × $60 + $0.20(200)

Answer Key

Question	Answer	APPLIED MATHEMATICS: Patterns, Functions, Algebra, Level A (cont.)
8	b	Rental fee for n days: $35n$. Mileage charges for x miles: $\$0.10(x - 100)$. Therefore, $T = 35n + 0.1(x - 100)$.
9	a	Rental fee for five days: $5(45)$. Mileage charges for x miles: $\$0.15(x - 200)$. Total cost: $5(45) + \$0.15(x - 200) = \$279$.
10	c	$\$40 \times 10 + \$15x = \$925$; $\$400 + \$15x = \$925$; $\$15x = \$525$; $x = 35$ hours
11	d	Amount working as a computer technician: $15x$. Amount working as a teacher: $40y$. Total amount: $T = 15x + 40y$.
12	b	$4x - 2 < 10$; $4x < 12$; $x < 3$; x can be any number less than 3
13	b	Four white tiles are used for every 3 feet. So, 12 white tiles (4×3) will be used for the first 9 feet. Then 2 more white tiles will be used in the last foot of the pattern: $12 + 2 = 14$.
14		**± 6** Let x be the missing number. Then $2x = \frac{72}{x}$; $2x^2 = 72$; $x^2 = 36$; $x = \pm 6$
15		**8** $\sqrt{2n} = 4$; $2n = 16$; $n = 8$
16		**1 mile** Convert 30 minutes to 0.5 hour. Solve the proportion: $\frac{12 \text{ miles}}{6 \text{ hours}} = \frac{x \text{ miles}}{0.5 \text{ hours}}$; $6x = 6$; $x = 1$ mile.
17		**8 numbers** The intersection of all whole numbers greater than or equal to 2 and all whole numbers less than or equal to 9 will satisfy both inequalities. The whole numbers are 2, 3, 4, 5, 6, 7, 8, and 9.
		APPLIED MATHEMATICS: Problem Solving and Reasoning, Level A
3	c	$\frac{36}{16} = 2.25$; $\frac{2.25}{18} = 0.125 = 12.5\%$
4	d	Twice the length of the shorter piece is $2x$. The longer piece (y) is one foot greater, or $y = 2x + 1$. This equation is equivalent to $2x = y - 1$.
5	c	$8 \times 60 = 480$; $(36 + 45 + 24 + 45 + 52 + 38 = 240)$; $480 - 240 = 240$
6	c	Men's Jeans should be $\$2,376$, not $\$2,200$: $\$52 - \$25 = \$27$; $88 \times \$27 = \$2,376$
7	a	The number of tiles to surround the pool is 84. The only expression equal to 84 is choice A. $(2 \times 31) + (2 \times 11) = 62 + 22 = 84$
8	c	Using the information given, one can determine the number of pages typed in one day. However, the pay per day cannot be determined without knowing the amount paid for each typed page.
9	a	Solving for r in the formula $i = Prt$, you obtain $r = \frac{i}{pt}$. The principal invested (P) is ($6 \times \$150$), or $\$900$. The time in years ($t$) is ($\frac{6}{12}$), or 0.5. The interest earned (i) is $\$24.75$. Substituting these values in the equation $r = \frac{i}{pt}$, you obtain $r = \frac{\$24.75}{\$900 \times 0.5}$
10	c	For every 10 weeks of training, the time decreases by 60 seconds. Therefore, for 5 weeks of training, the time should decrease by 30 seconds. For 45 weeks of training, the time should be $(7:30 - 0:30)$, or 7:00.

Answer Key

| --- | --- | --- |
11		**The charge is not correct.** The charge should be $44.50. [12 + 3(5) + 5(3.5) = 12 + 15 + 17.50 = 44.50]
12		**400 feet** 7,500 ÷ 150 = 50; 2(150) + 2(50) = 300 + 100 = 400
13		**40 feet** $50{,}240 = (3.14)r^2(40)$; $50{,}240 = 125.6r^2$; $\frac{50{,}240}{125.6} = r^2$; $400 = r^2$; $20 = r$; $d = 2r$; $d = 2(20)$; $d = 40$
14		**100 feet** $\frac{10}{20} = \frac{50}{x}$; $10x = 1{,}000$; $x = \frac{1{,}000}{10}$; $x = 100$

Building Skills with TABE®
Tests of Adult Basic Education

Student Answer Booklet

Level A: Math Computation and Applied Mathematics

Name: _____   Date: _____

Organization/Program: _____

1

MATH COMPUTATION   Decimals

1 (a) (b) (c) (d) (e)   8 (a) (b) (c) (d) (e)

2 (a) (b) (c) (d) (e)   9 (a) (b) (c) (d) (e)

3 (a) (b) (c) (d) (e)   10 (a) (b) (c) (d) (e)

4 (a) (b) (c) (d) (e)   11 _____

5 (a) (b) (c) (d) (e)   12 _____

6 (a) (b) (c) (d) (e)   13 _____

7 (a) (b) (c) (d) (e)   14 _____

MATH COMPUTATION   Fractions

1 (a) (b) (c) (d) (e)   8 (a) (b) (c) (d) (e)

2 (a) (b) (c) (d) (e)   9 (a) (b) (c) (d) (e)

3 (a) (b) (c) (d) (e)   10 (a) (b) (c) (d) (e)

4 (a) (b) (c) (d) (e)   11 _____

5 (a) (b) (c) (d) (e)   12 _____

6 (a) (b) (c) (d) (e)   13 _____

7 (a) (b) (c) (d) (e)   14 _____

MATH COMPUTATION   Integers

1 (a) (b) (c) (d) (e)   8 (a) (b) (c) (d) (e)

2 (a) (b) (c) (d) (e)   9 (a) (b) (c) (d) (e)

3 (a) (b) (c) (d) (e)   10 (a) (b) (c) (d) (e)

4 (a) (b) (c) (d) (e)   11 _____

5 (a) (b) (c) (d) (e)   12 _____

6 (a) (b) (c) (d) (e)   13 _____

7 (a) (b) (c) (d) (e)   14 _____

MATH COMPUTATION   Percents

1 ⓐ ⓑ ⓒ ⓓ ⓔ   8 ⓐ ⓑ ⓒ ⓓ ⓔ

2 ⓐ ⓑ ⓒ ⓓ ⓔ   9 ⓐ ⓑ ⓒ ⓓ ⓔ

3 ⓐ ⓑ ⓒ ⓓ ⓔ   10 _____

4 ⓐ ⓑ ⓒ ⓓ ⓔ   11 _____

5 ⓐ ⓑ ⓒ ⓓ ⓔ   12 _____

6 ⓐ ⓑ ⓒ ⓓ ⓔ   13 _____

7 ⓐ ⓑ ⓒ ⓓ ⓔ

MATH COMPUTATION   Order of Operations

1 ⓐ ⓑ ⓒ ⓓ ⓔ   8 ⓐ ⓑ ⓒ ⓓ ⓔ

2 ⓐ ⓑ ⓒ ⓓ ⓔ   9 ⓐ ⓑ ⓒ ⓓ ⓔ

3 ⓐ ⓑ ⓒ ⓓ ⓔ   10 ⓐ ⓑ ⓒ ⓓ ⓔ

4 ⓐ ⓑ ⓒ ⓓ ⓔ   11 _____

5 ⓐ ⓑ ⓒ ⓓ ⓔ   12 _____

6 ⓐ ⓑ ⓒ ⓓ ⓔ   13 _____

7 ⓐ ⓑ ⓒ ⓓ ⓔ   14 _____

MATH COMPUTATION   Algebraic Operations

1 ⓐ ⓑ ⓒ ⓓ ⓔ   8 ⓐ ⓑ ⓒ ⓓ ⓔ

2 ⓐ ⓑ ⓒ ⓓ ⓔ   9 ⓐ ⓑ ⓒ ⓓ ⓔ

3 ⓐ ⓑ ⓒ ⓓ ⓔ   10 ⓐ ⓑ ⓒ ⓓ ⓔ

4 ⓐ ⓑ ⓒ ⓓ ⓔ   11 _____

5 ⓐ ⓑ ⓒ ⓓ ⓔ   12 _____

6 ⓐ ⓑ ⓒ ⓓ ⓔ   13 _____

7 ⓐ ⓑ ⓒ ⓓ ⓔ   14 _____

APPLIED MATHEMATICS   Number and Number Operations

1 ⓐ ⓑ ⓒ ⓓ	7 ⓐ ⓑ ⓒ ⓓ	13 ⓐ ⓑ ⓒ ⓓ	19 _____
2 ⓐ ⓑ ⓒ ⓓ	8 ⓐ ⓑ ⓒ ⓓ	14 ⓐ ⓑ ⓒ ⓓ	20 _____
3 ⓐ ⓑ ⓒ ⓓ	9 ⓐ ⓑ ⓒ ⓓ	15 ⓐ ⓑ ⓒ ⓓ	21 _____
4 ⓐ ⓑ ⓒ ⓓ	10 ⓐ ⓑ ⓒ ⓓ	16 ⓐ ⓑ ⓒ ⓓ	22 _____
5 ⓐ ⓑ ⓒ ⓓ	11 ⓐ ⓑ ⓒ ⓓ	17 ⓐ ⓑ ⓒ ⓓ	23 _____
6 ⓐ ⓑ ⓒ ⓓ	12 ⓐ ⓑ ⓒ ⓓ	18 ⓐ ⓑ ⓒ ⓓ	24 _____

APPLIED MATHEMATICS   Computation in Context

1 ⓐ ⓑ ⓒ ⓓ	9 ⓐ ⓑ ⓒ ⓓ
2 ⓐ ⓑ ⓒ ⓓ	10 ⓐ ⓑ ⓒ ⓓ
3 ⓐ ⓑ ⓒ ⓓ	11 _____
4 ⓐ ⓑ ⓒ ⓓ	12 _____
5 ⓐ ⓑ ⓒ ⓓ	13 _____
6 ⓐ ⓑ ⓒ ⓓ	14 _____
7 ⓐ ⓑ ⓒ ⓓ	15 _____
8 ⓐ ⓑ ⓒ ⓓ	

APPLIED MATHEMATICS   Estimation

1 (a) (b) (c) (d)   5 (a) (b) (c) (d)   9 (a) (b) (c) (d)   13 _____

2 (a) (b) (c) (d)   6 (a) (b) (c) (d)   10 (a) (b) (c) (d)   14 _____

3 (a) (b) (c) (d)   7 (a) (b) (c) (d)   11 (a) (b) (c) (d)   15 _____

4 (a) (b) (c) (d)   8 (a) (b) (c) (d)   12 (a) (b) (c) (d)   16 _____

APPLIED MATHEMATICS   Measurement

1 (a) (b) (c) (d)   5 (a) (b) (c) (d)   9 (a) (b) (c) (d)   13 _____

2 (a) (b) (c) (d)   6 (a) (b) (c) (d)   10 (a) (b) (c) (d)   14 _____

3 (a) (b) (c) (d)   7 (a) (b) (c) (d)   11 (a) (b) (c) (d)   15 _____

4 (a) (b) (c) (d)   8 (a) (b) (c) (d)   12 (a) (b) (c) (d)   16 _____

APPLIED MATHEMATICS   Geometry and Spatial Sense

1 Ⓐ ⓑ ⓒ ⓓ   6 Ⓐ ⓑ ⓒ ⓓ   11 Ⓐ ⓑ ⓒ ⓓ   16 _____

2 Ⓐ ⓑ ⓒ ⓓ   7 Ⓐ ⓑ ⓒ ⓓ   12 Ⓐ ⓑ ⓒ ⓓ   17 _____

3 Ⓐ ⓑ ⓒ ⓓ   8 Ⓐ ⓑ ⓒ ⓓ   13 Ⓐ ⓑ ⓒ ⓓ   18 _____

4 Ⓐ ⓑ ⓒ ⓓ   9 Ⓐ ⓑ ⓒ ⓓ   14 Ⓐ ⓑ ⓒ ⓓ   19 _____

5 Ⓐ ⓑ ⓒ ⓓ   10 Ⓐ ⓑ ⓒ ⓓ   15 Ⓐ ⓑ ⓒ ⓓ

APPLIED MATHEMATICS   Data Analysis

1 Ⓐ ⓑ ⓒ ⓓ   5 Ⓐ ⓑ ⓒ ⓓ   9 Ⓐ ⓑ ⓒ ⓓ   13 _____

2 Ⓐ ⓑ ⓒ ⓓ   6 Ⓐ ⓑ ⓒ ⓓ   10 Ⓐ ⓑ ⓒ ⓓ   14 _____

3 Ⓐ ⓑ ⓒ ⓓ   7 Ⓐ ⓑ ⓒ ⓓ   11 Ⓐ ⓑ ⓒ ⓓ   15 _____

4 Ⓐ ⓑ ⓒ ⓓ   8 Ⓐ ⓑ ⓒ ⓓ   12 Ⓐ ⓑ ⓒ ⓓ   16 _____

APPLIED MATHEMATICS   Statistics and Probability

1 Ⓐ ⓑ ⓒ ⓓ   6 Ⓐ ⓑ ⓒ ⓓ   11 _____

2 Ⓐ ⓑ ⓒ ⓓ   7 Ⓐ ⓑ ⓒ ⓓ   12 _____

3 Ⓐ ⓑ ⓒ ⓓ   8 Ⓐ ⓑ ⓒ ⓓ   13 _____

4 Ⓐ ⓑ ⓒ ⓓ   9 Ⓐ ⓑ ⓒ ⓓ   14 _____

5 Ⓐ ⓑ ⓒ ⓓ   10 Ⓐ ⓑ ⓒ ⓓ

APPLIED MATHEMATICS   Patterns, Functions, Algebra

1 (a) (b) (c) (d)   7 (a) (b) (c) (d)   13 (a) (b) (c) (d)

2 (a) (b) (c) (d)   8 (a) (b) (c) (d)   14 _____

3 (a) (b) (c) (d)   9 (a) (b) (c) (d)   15 _____

4 (a) (b) (c) (d)   10 (a) (b) (c) (d)   16 _____

5 (a) (b) (c) (d)   11 (a) (b) (c) (d)   17 _____

6 (a) (b) (c) (d)   12 (a) (b) (c) (d)

APPLIED MATHEMATICS   Problem Solving and Reasoning

1 (a) (b) (c) (d)   6 (a) (b) (c) (d)   11 _____

2 (a) (b) (c) (d)   7 (a) (b) (c) (d)   12 _____

3 (a) (b) (c) (d)   8 (a) (b) (c) (d)   13 _____

4 (a) (b) (c) (d)   9 (a) (b) (c) (d)   14 _____

5 (a) (b) (c) (d)   10 (a) (b) (c) (d)